A Fourth Book of 101 School Assembly Stories

A Fourth Book of 101 School Assembly Stories

Written, selected and compiled
by
ANN D. LOESCHER

foulsham educational
LONDON • NEW YORK • TORONTO • SYDNEY

foulsham

Bennetts Close, Cippenham, Berkshire SL1 5AP

Also published by Foulsham:
101 School Assembly Stories
A Second Book of 101 School Assembly Stories
and
A Third Book of 101 School Assembly Stories

ISBN 0-572-01878-9
Text & Artwork © W. Foulsham & Co. Ltd. 1993

Phototypeset in Great Britain by Typesetting Solutions, Slough, Berkshire
Printed and bound in Great Britain by
Redwood Books, Trowbridge, Wiltshire

Contents

Acknowledgements

Despite every effort it has not been possible to trace the source of all these stories. If an author's copyright has been infringed sincere regrets are tendered.

The Publishers are grateful for permission to use the following stories in this collection:

Langston Hughes	Adapted from an original story by Margaret Loescher.
Rama and Sita	Adapted from an original story by Claire Loescher.

The following were adapted from original stories by Hedley Edwards: A Change of Heart; Abraham and Isaac; Jesus Appears to his Disciples; O Christmas Tree; God's Promises to Noah; The House with Golden Windows; Sadako Sasaki; Greed; Palm Sunday; No Charge.

Nasim's Eid Gift	Adapted from an original story by Michael Herschell.
Off to a Slow Start	Adapted from an original story by G. L. Dawson.
My Teacher Hates Me	Adapted from an original story by D. J. Marl.
The Traffic Jam and The Riddle	Adapted from original stories by Jennifer Burnap.
The Mole and Cloud in the Wind	from GREEN PIECES by Bob Loosemore.
Vagabonds	from SELECTED POEMS by Langston Hughes. Copyright 1947 by Langston Hughes. Reprinted by permission of Alfred A. Knopf, Inc.
The Wind of Change	Copyright Rod McKuen/Stanyan Records.
Fireworks	by James Reeves from BLACKBIRD IN THE LILAC, Oxford University Press, Oxford, reproduced in FOR TODAY AND TOMORROW — AN ANTHOLOGY OF POEMS FOR YOUNG PEOPLE complied by Howard Sergent, Evans Bros, 1974.
London Trees	by Margaret Stanley Wrench from FOR TODAY AND TOMORROW — AN ANTHOLOGY OF POEMS FOR YOUNG PEOPLE compiled by Howard Sergent, Evans Bros, 1974.
Cats	from WATCH FOR THE WIND. Copyright Rod McKuen/ Montcalm Productions.
Television Aerials	by Stanley Cook, from DRUMMING IN THE SKY, BBC Books.

Photograph of Lech Walewsa on page 28 copyright News Focus.

Photographs of Daley Thompson, Nelson Mandela (by H. Gautier), Amelia Earhart, The Dalai Lama and Michael Landon (with Lorne Green) on pages 9, 24, 26, 51, 55, copyright Camera Press.

Illustrations throughout this book were by Colin Grey and Mei Lim.

TRUE STORIES

Daley Thompson, Decathlete

Do you know a child like this - can't sit still, often in trouble for fighting, hogs the ball on the football pitch? This was Daley Thompson. Daley just didn't seem able to work very well in a group. He liked being the centre of attention and was a bit of a show-off. These qualities in a person can lead him into trouble but Daley was lucky. Instead, his life took a turn for the better when he started training to be an athlete in the most gruelling of all individual athletic tests, the decathlon.

Most tests of athletic prowess require a person to be really good at one thing - say running, jumping or throwing. But the 'decathlon' requires a person to be good at ten different events. The name 'decathlon' is a combination of two Greek words: 'deka' for ten and 'athlos' for struggle. The decathlon was included in the early Greek games that were the ancestors of today's Olympic Games. The decathlon is tried over two days, with five events on each day. On the first day the entrant is tested at sprinting 100 metres, long jump, shot putt, high jump and 400 metres run. The second day's tests include 110 metres high hurdles, discus throw, pole vault, javelin throw and then running 1500 metres. During the two days, the competitors are

9

awarded points for each event according to their performances. At the end of the event the points are totalled to determine the winner. The decathlon series of events tests the greatest athletes and anyone who does it even moderately well can call himself or herself a true athlete in the traditional sense of the word. Daley Thompson didn't just do moderately well, he was wonderful!

But not at first. Daley's first love was football and he wanted to be a professional. He was very good at it, but he was not a good team player. He wanted a sport at which he could excel as an individual. While he was in training for football, his coach had suggested that he go along to his local athletic club to get some running practice. There, Daley took an instant liking to athletics and began to show real promise. He was a natural athlete. But he still had a long way to go. Daley hated to lose and when, in his first big race, he was only placed fourth, he was ready to quit athletics, there and then.

Fortunately for Daley, someone had been watching him who believed he had potential. Bob Mortimer convinced Daley he should stay in athletics and he became his first coach. Daley showed real ability in running and jumping events and decided he wanted to be the best all-round athlete in the world. He began to train seriously for the decathlon.

Training to be really good at sport takes devotion and drive. It takes all an athlete's spare time to keep fit and train. A person has to really *want* to be the best if he or she is ever going to *be* the best. Even though Daley was still only a teenager, he had the

tenacity and coaching support he needed to keep working for his dream.

Daley had his eye on the Olympic Games that were to be held in Montreal, Canada in July 1976. He made it through the British Olympic trials and, at only 17 years old, was awarded a place on the team. He knew it was not likely he would

win a medal at the Olympics but it was a real achievement to be good enough to be on the team, and just competing would be wonderful.

Daley used his first Olympics as a learning experience. he greatly admired the performance of the gold medal winner, the American decathlete, Bruce Jenner.

Daley's career continued, with both ups and downs, and each time he lost he thought of quitting but he always tried again. The first gold medal he won was in the European Junior Championships in 1977. Then in 1978 he won a gold at the Commonwealth Games. Daley, a real extrovert, loved being watched by the crowds at these big events. Success was now changing him from a pugnacious boy into a cheerful and friendly person. His smile and genuine good nature won him a place in the hearts of his fans and his fellow athletes. His winning personality and his winning performances boosted public interest in the decathlon.

As the 1980 Moscow Olympic Games drew near, Daley thought he was ready. This was not to be a learning experience. This time Daley would not just compete. This time Daley had set his heart on the Olympic gold. And he did it. He won the gold medal for Britain with a total of 8,495 points. And he would go on to win gold again in 1984 at Los Angeles and 1988 in Seoul, making him the only decathlete to win the gold medal in three successive Olympic Games.

Walls

Throughout history people have built walls to keep out their enemies and to protect their own people within them. Even the walls of our houses do this for us.

One of the most famous walls ever built was the one around the ancient city of Jericho. We can read about the battle of Jericho in the Old Testament. The city of Jericho stood in the way of the Israelites as they entered the land of Canaan. It's walls were very high and thick. God told Joshua how to make the walls come down. He said seven priests should march around the outside of the city walls every day for six days. He said they must blow their rams' horn trumpets as they went. Joshua told the Israelites to do as God commanded and when they had, the walls of Jericho crumbled and the Israelites took the city. The wall was no longer there to keep enemies out.

A much longer wall is the Great Wall of China. It is about 2,000 years old and was built by the Chinese in order to keep out nomadic tribes that lived in the lands to the north. The wall is 1,400 miles long, between 6 and 9 metres high and 2½ to 3 metres wide. It took about eighteen years to complete. Many Chinese died working on it and they were buried within the wall. It is built of solid stone and has a road running along its top with raised edges that are crenellated like the tops of some castles. Every few hundred yards, there is a big square tower, also with crenellations. The whole thing looks like an enormously long castle, very strong and rather mysterious. The wall follows the rise and fall of the high ground, snaking over hilltops in the hilly north of China. It must have made the Chinese feel safe. However, invading armies did get over or through the wall, and people wanting to trade peacefully with the Chinese were allowed through at special doorways. Of course, the Chinese always had to guard their wall so special patrols lived near it and kept watch from the towers or patrolled along the top. If an invading force was spotted, fires were lit on top of the towers as an alarm signal so the defending forces could assemble to fight off the attack. The Great Wall of China is still there and many tourists visit it every year.

Another wall that was built to keep out waring tribes is Hadrian's Wall in the north of England. Hadrian was one of the Emperors of Rome when the Romans ruled Britain, about 2,000 years ago. The Romans had fought and conquered the people in England but they had had a great deal of difficulty subduing fierce, nomadic tribes that roamed in Scotland at that time. So the Romans decided to draw a line to mark the northern limit of their own territory. They built Hadrian's Wall along that line. It runs for 73 miles (about 120 kilometres), coast to coast, right across northern England. This wall was not as big as the Great Wall of China and it took very many soldiers to guard it against invasion. Signal towers and forts for the Roman soldiers to live in were built at intervals

along it. The Roman legions marched along the wall from fort to fort keeping watch and making a show of force. In some places Hadrian's Wall was made of stone, in other places it was built of turf. The Romans dug a deep ditch along the wall to make it even harder to scale. Hadrian's Wall still exists today, though parts of it are broken down. People enjoy visiting it as it is interesting in itself and most of it runs through beautiful countryside.

More recently, a wall was built especially to keep some people in. This was the Berlin Wall. After the Second World War, Germany was divided into East and West Germany. It's capital city, Berlin, was also divided this way. East Berlin came under communist rule and West Berlin was under the democratic rule of West Germany. Life in East Berlin was very hard. many people there had friends or family in the West. Lots of people wanted to escape to West Berlin but the East German government did not want its people leaving. If they let people go, they thought, there would be no one left to do the important jobs that had to be tackled if their country was to move forward. In order to stop people escaping to West Berlin, the East German Government built a wall all the way across the city. The wall went across streets and in some places the city's buildings formed part of it, with their doors and windows bricked up. All along the wall there were huge spirals of barbed wire, with minefields in front of it. It looked more like a battlefield than a city. Some people refused to be discouraged from seeking freedom in the West and they tried to get over the wall to safety in West Berlin. But the wall was guarded by East German troops who had strict orders to shoot anyone trying to escape to the West. Many people lost their lives trying to do just that.

The Berlin Wall has now been torn down. When the European communist governments began to fall in 1989, people decided the wall had to come down too. One autumn evening a group of West Berliners began to knock the wall down. No one shot at them. The East German soldiers just watched. Word spread along both sides of the wall and crowds of people congregated to help and watch. They began pulling big pieces of the wall away and they finally made a way through. People rushed through the opening and hugged each other. They cheered and sang and wept. It was a moment when history changed direction. A country which had been divided into two was able to unite again.

Langston Hughes

Langston Hughes was a black American poet. He was born in 1902. It was a time when black Americans were no longer slaves but most lived in terrible poverty and without basic rights. The difficulties Langston endured are still being suffered today by many black people.

Langston's father had studied to be a lawyer but when he asked to take the bar examinations he was told 'No Negroes'. This discouraged him so much that he gave up and ran away to Mexico, leaving his young wife and baby Langston. Langston's father remained bitter towards the United States for the rest of his life. The attitude of American whites toward blacks has wasted many capable people like Langston's father.

Carrie Hughes, Langston's mother, had a hard time. For a black woman, finding a job was very difficult and she had little Langston to take care of as well. She managed as well as she could until he was seven and then she decided she must put him in the care of his grandmother. His grandmother was quite a remarkable woman. She had been the first black woman to attend Oberlin College and she knew the value of education so Langston was sent to school. His grandmother told Langston stories, mostly about freedom and slaves. She also introduced him to great literature.

Sadly for Langston, his grandmother died when he was twelve. But friends of hers took him into their home and treated him as their own son. During this time he worked at a hotel, cleaning out spitoons and only earning the equivalent of about 25 pence a week.

Langston went to Central High School in Cleveland, Ohio, where there were children from many ethnic backgrounds. Langston learned that many people are prejudiced against all minorities but being black was hardest. The colour of your skin was immediately obvious, and made you a target for prejudiced people.

There were not many black students in his high school. Langston made a point of meeting black people elsewhere and getting to know them. The experiences in Langston Hughes' early life helped him develop into the poet he was later to become.

Meanwhile, Langston's father had made a great deal of money as a rancher in Mexico. He thought there was no future for black people in America. He tried to persuade Langston to become an engineer and join him in Mexico. But Langston wanted to go to Columbia University in New York City so he could study to become a writer and he managed to convince his father to give him the money. However, studying at Columbia was not all that Langston had hoped it would be. None of his professors ever talked about things that concern black people and after one year there, Langston withdrew. He had found that the time he spent in Harlem, a black section of New York City, was more educational than the time he spent in classes at Columbia.

Langston's ability as a poet had been recognized only by young, black people like himself but one day he met the famous American poet Vachel Lindsay. Langston was working in a hotel diningroom when Vachel Lindsay came in. Langston recognized Lindsay and quickly wrote out some of his poems and left them by Lindsay's plate. After reading the poems, Lindsay wrote about Langston in the newspaper and praised his work and he became more widely known.

Langston wanted to travel and he managed to get a job as a messboy on a boat going to Africa. It was hard work but Langston wanted to go to Africa to learn more about black culture. In Africa, he learned that he was not black enough. He had had a white grandparent and so he was not as black as the Africans of pure ancestry. He felt then as if he did not belong to either race but this experience taught him

solidarity with his fellow black Americans. Langston went to Africa because he thought he was going 'home'. He was disappointed to find that there were whites there, too, and that there were many of the same racial tensions in Africa as there were in America.

When Langston went back to America he became part of the literary movement known as the Black Renaissance. This was a group of young black writers and artists who knew and encouraged each other in many ways. Langston's poems began to be published, often in magazines. For a poet or writer or artist, creating something is exciting and of primary importance but having your work published means you can share your feelings with other people. When those people come to appreciate your work, you feel fulfilled - your work of art is completed.

Langston Hughes wrote poetry that showed what it was like to be black in

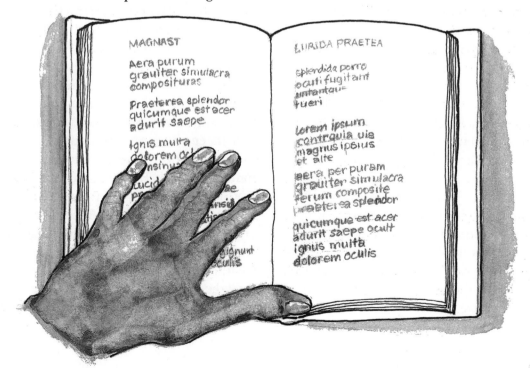

America instead of white. He wrote in dialect, with the rhythm of the blues and jazz in his poetry. Although black writers like Langston had an audience, most people still discounted blacks and did not fully appreciate the value of their contribution to American culture. To teach people about black American culture, Langston often visited schools to read and talk about his poetry. He wanted to teach white children the value of black culture and to teach black children that they could achieve something in their lives. He wanted to teach all children that a person's race is not the most important thing about him or her. He wanted them to realise that every person is valuable and that it is the variety of human beings and their various cultures that makes the world a rich and exciting place to live. These lessons are still being learned today.

Tragedy in Space

Cape Canaveral, Florida, 28th January 1986. The United States space shuttle Challenger is ready for take-off. It sits on its launch pad in the unusually cold but clear winter morning. The astronauts are really hoping that today will be the day. There have been three postponements of the flight already because of small things going wrong.

Even though there have been twenty-four previous flights of Challenger, this one is special. For the first time ever there will be a private citizen on board. She is not in the Air Force. She is not a NASA scientist. She is just an ordinary person - a school-teacher from the state of New Hampshire. Her name is Christa McAuliffe. Her husband and children and her class at school are all watching with happy anticipation.

There are six other astronauts on the Challenger crew. The commander is Dick Scobee. Michael Smith is the pilot. There are three mission specialists on Challenger's crew, another young woman named Judith Resnik, Ellison Onizuka who is a Japanese American, and Ronald McNair who is a Black American.

Finally, the decision is made to go ahead with the flight in spite of the very cold weather. This proves to be a terrible mistake.

It takes more than astronauts to make a

space flight. There are many more people who work on the ground. There are the scientists and designers who work for years beforehand to design the vehicle and develop the fuel. There are people who maintain every tiny part of the space shuttle. There are people who check every detail of the planned flight and others who are in charge of the special communications system that during the mission will keep the Challenger in touch with people on the ground. All these people have very special and important jobs to do. The success of the mission and the lives of the astronauts depend on all the people doing their jobs, no matter how small, the very best way they can. But today someone isn't quite careful enough. Someone who has a vital decision to make isn't cautious. It will lead to tragedy.

The crew are excited and happy as they make their way to Challenger. They have shiny globular helmets with darkened wraparound windscreens. They wear silver suits with the NASA logo on them. They are looking forward to working on this mission.

Crowds have gathered a safe distance from the launch pad with binoculars and telescopes to watch the lift-off. People are particularly excited about this launch because an ordinary person like themselves is on board. And the rest of the crew are representative of the wide variety of people who live in the United States. Teachers and school-children across America are watching on television sets because Christa McAuliffe, a teacher, is on board.

The sky is a beautiful, clear blue. But it is

too cold. Challenger's countdown goes smoothly. There is ignition with its fire and billowing smoke, and at 11.30 a.m. Challenger lifts off. The heads of the people watching go slowly up, following the bright smoke-trail Challenger leaves as it climbs. Challenger has been up about a minute when mission control tell Commander Scobee, 'Challenger go at throttle-up.' The Commander is expecting that and he replies, 'Roger, go at throttle-up.' Pilot Michael Smith says, 'Uh-oh.' But no one hears him. Suddenly, Challenger explodes in an enormous fireball and disintegrates. The horrified watchers on the ground see pieces of flaming space shuttle spin widely out of the explosion and fall into the Atlantic Ocean. The crew all die instantly.

Afterwards, the scientists of the Challenger programme investigate and discover that a fuel leak caused the explosion and that cold weather was to blame for the leak. They come to realize how a wrong decision was made. They know the facts of why the tragedy happened.

So, people can talk to each other about the tragedy and explain it in terms of what went wrong but no one can really answer the question that they ask themselves and each other: 'Why did it have to happen?' Why do bad things happen to good people?

The Brontë Sisters

When Patrick Brontë walked through the door of Haworth Parsonage in June 1826 with a box of wooden soldiers for his young son, little did he know what it would lead to.

Charlotte, Emily and Ann Brontë and their brother Branwell had always been close and loved walking on the moors and playing together. When the box of soldiers arrived for Branwell, the three sisters each claimed one for herself. It was the beginning of long hours of play, of made-up characters and imaginary lands. It was the starting point for the stories and poems that Charlotte, Emily and Anne would write throughout their lives. They made their stories into tiny books and carefully illustrated them. They drew maps of their imagined lands and gave their heroes and heroines remarkable lives. The game went on for years. As they grew, the stories grew too, becoming longer and more true to life.

The Brontë children had difficult childhoods but the closeness of the family helped them through it. Their mother died when they were all quite young. Then the two eldest children Maria and Elizabeth, died of tuberculosis within a month of each other. An aunt came to help Patrick Brontë look after his children and after a period of adjustment, she adopted the family. Later, a local girl called Tabitha

Aykroyd came to be a servant at the Parsonage and her good humour and kindness towards the children brightened their lives.

Patrick Brontë gave his children a varied education at home, introducing them to a broad range of reading matter. The Parsonage was a grim house in a grim mill town and built on a windy hill next to an overcrowded cemetery. But the miles of open moor came right up to the back of the house and the Brontë children spent many hours walking and playing on them.

It is rare to find a household that produces one or two great writers but the Brontë household contained three. And this was in Victorian times when women were thought to be less able than men at most things. They certainly were not expected to write novels for publication. So when the Brontë sisters decided to send their poems and stories to publishers they signed themselves with men's names. They called themselves Currer, Ellis and Acton Bell, keeping their first initials the same. Considering how much they liked to play games about made-up characters, they must have had great fun making believe they were someone else. The reading public was surprised to find three brothers, all of whom wrote such good books. How much more surprised they were when they learned that the three were in fact sisters.

Each of the Brontë sisters tried working or studying away from home but it was never very successful and they were always happy to go home to the Parsonage where they enjoyed each other's company and did their best writing.

Sadly, the three talented and sensitive sisters all died young. Anne was only 29, Emily 30, and Charlotte lived to be 39.

Their best novels are still read and enjoyed today. Perhaps you may have heard of *Jane Eyre* by Charlotte or *Wuthering Heights* by Emily. Both of these have been made into films.

Willem Kolff

At either side of your spine, just above your waist, deep inside your back are two very important organs. They are your kidneys. They have the very important job of cleaning waste products out of your blood. If they stopped working your body would soon be poisoned and you would die. Or you would have done if it hadn't been for a Dutch doctor named Willem Kolff.

Willem Kolff was born in 1911 and he became a doctor like his father and his grandfather before him. When Willem was working in a hospital, a young man died of kidney failure. Willem thought such a tragedy might have been avoided. He knew what the kidneys did and thought if he could find a way of cleaning the blood of people whose kidneys weren't functioning he could save their lives.

World War II interrupted his research on the problem because there was so much else for the young doctor to do. He realised there was a great need for blood to transfuse into wounded soldiers and civilians and he established the first blood bank.

After the Germans invaded his country he continued to work at a hospital in the Netherlands and there the germ of his idea for an artificial kidney kept growing in his mind. He knew it would be a valuable invention and he did not want the Nazis to learn about it. So he continued to do his research and development in secrecy. Finally, using salty water, sausage skins

and bits and pieces of other materials and with the secret help of other patriotic Dutchmen, the first kidney machine was developed. It was huge and though it helped kidney patients temporarily, sadly, it did not save their lives.

At that point some people might have given up. Not Willem Kolff. He continued to work on his idea, believing it was the right approach and that it only needed refining. He developed new machines and, finally, in 1945, one of them saved the life of a woman who had been near death. At last Willem's years of work had paid off.

Willem continued to improve his machine, and made it much smaller and better. Nowadays, surgeons have learned how to transplant healthy kidneys into ill patients but there is still a need for Willem's invention. Patients often must wait months even years for healthy kidneys to become available for a kidney transplant operation.

Having made a success of one medical invention, Willem might have rested on his laurels. He might have taken the well-earned praise and decided he had done enough. Not Willem Kolff. He went on to invent a heart-lung machine. A heart-lung machine is very important during open-heart surgery, when the patient's own heart and lungs cannot function. Then the heart-lung machine takes over. It makes blood continue to circulate round the body and oxygen to enter the blood. So it keeps the patient alive while the surgeon works. He also invented an artificial heart that has been used in people whose own hearts can no longer work. And he has done pioneer work on a tiny camera which has electrode implants in the brains of blind people in an effort to help them see. His tireless curiosity and inventiveness will continue to benefit people long after he is gone.

Roads

A traveller in the 18th century wrote to a friend about being in a horse-drawn coach. 'I had a very bad journey into Buckinghamshire, and like to have been overturned twenty times. The passengers alighted several times, up to the mid-legs in dirt, and walked for miles in dirty, splashy ways.' He was probably very lucky he wasn't asked to push as well. Roads in those days were terrible. They were deep in mud when the weather was wet and rutted and holed when it was dry. Going on a long journey by road could be a very dangerous undertaking.

It wasn't only people that had a rough ride. If a potter took crockery to market by road he would be lucky to get most of it there unbroken. Because of the poor state of roads, the rail and canal systems began to be developed.

Britain had not always had such bad roads. When the Romans occupied Britain they built a network of very good roads. Some of these are still in use today as the foundations of modern roads. Many of the long, very straight roads you see on maps are built over the old Roman roads. The Romans laid several layers of different kinds of stone and soil to make their roads sound, and they curved the top slightly so water would run off the road surface into the gutters at either side. We still design roads this way today. If the Roman road was to be used only by foot soldiers it was called an *iter* and was only 5 feet wide (about 1½ metres). An *actus* was 7 feet wide (about 2 metres) and that meant a horse-drawn vehicle could use it. The widest and busiest kind of road was called a *via* and was 14 feet wide (about 4½ metres). It took a great deal of time and manpower to build all the roads the Romans needed and they built them to last.

After the Romans left Britain, the road system deteriorated and for centuries many travellers made miserable journeys. Carts and coaches overturned or got stuck in the mud. When they did move, they bumped uncomfortably over stones and into holes and ruts. If a traveller chose to go by horseback he might have to do a good part of the journey on foot and would probably have to get his horse out of the mud more than once. Something had to be done.

'Blind Jack of Knaresborough' was one of the people who decided he would do something about the roads. His real name was John Metcalf and he lived about two hundred years ago. He had had a dangerous disease called smallpox when he was six and it left him totally blind. But he grew up to have some very good ideas about better roads. He needed only to walk across a piece of ground and feel the best route for a road to take. He developed a simple and effective way to build a road across marshy ground. There was a lot of heather growing nearby and he told the workmen to tie the heather twigs into bundles and lay them in a certain way in the marsh where the road was to be built. Then he had them lay the stone layers of the road on top of the heather. The road

actually floated across the marsh with woody heather keeping it from sinking. His road stayed dry.

At about the same time lived Thomas Telford and John McAdam. Thomas was particularly famous for building bridges. He designed and directed the building of over 1,000 bridges in Britain. He also built canals and docks. His most important road is still in use today. John was best known for designing roads and finding the best combinations of materials. A material still in use today for building some roads is called macadam and is named after him. Like Romans, Thomas Telford and John MacAdam built roads that lasted.

The network of roads and motorways in Britain today can take us almost anywhere we want to go. But tucked away in secret places there are still green lanes and ridgeways. These are the remains of roads older than the Roman roads. Some of them are the oldest in all of Europe and they are still there for you to walk along. Perhaps one day you will walk the Pennine Way or The Ridgeway.

Nelson Mandela

Sunday, the 11th of February 1990, four o'clock in the afternoon and the world held its breath. People watched their television screens and stayed near to their radios waiting for news of the world's most famous political prisoner: Nelson Mandela.

Nelson Mandela had been held in prison in South Africa for twenty-seven years because he refused to denounce his politics and his principles of trying to obtain rights and justice for black people. The South African government had offered him his freedom a number of times if he would promise to leave the country and never try to lead its people again. He always refused. Now he had won. He was being set free without condition.

Nelson Mandela is a black man whose country, South Africa, has persecuted and punished its black and coloured people in order to ensure that power and wealth remain with the whites. The policy called apartheid which is practiced in South Africa is a policy of keeping blacks and whites separate. The white people of South Africa are wealthier and freer than the blacks and coloureds. They are a much smaller population but they control the government and the economy so it is very difficult for anyone who is not white to have a comfortable life.

All his life Nelson Mandela had worked

to help his fellow blacks fight against apartheid and its unfair laws. People who were opposed to apartheid were inspired by his intelligence, kindness and firm belief in equality and freedom for all peoples.

He became a lawyer and defended blacks who had been arrested under the laws of apartheid. He helped to organize many non-violent protests such as strikes and meetings. He always reminded his followers that violence was not the way to get what they wanted.

But the South African government itself used violence against unarmed blacks as a matter of policy. They beat, whipped and arrested protestors. They even shot into crowds of unarmed people, killing and injuring men, women and children.

Finally, Nelson and others who had always insisted on non-violent protest decided it was hopeless to protest and risk death and not to fight back. Nelson sacrificed his principles of non-violence and agreed that the blacks had to fight back.

Before this, Nelson had been imprisoned and silenced for speaking out about his beliefs and now he had once again

become a hunted man. The South African government saw him as a threat and accused him of wanting to overthrow the government. They hunted him and his fellow black leaders. Nelson moved about the country in disguise, organizing meetings and making speeches, avoiding the government spies and police.

Finally, on 5th August 1962, Nelson Mandela was caught. he was put on trial with other black leaders for trying to start a violent revolution. Nelson spoke eloquently on the prisoners' behalf, explaining how hard they had tried not to use violence and how the government had forced them to do so. Protests about the unfair way the trial was being run and support for the prisoners came in from all over the world. This pressure probably saved the accused men from being sentenced to death. Instead, they were given life imprisonment.

Nelson served twenty-seven years of that sentence and all the time he was in prison he continued to be a caring person who always had time to listen and give advice to others. Even his guards came to like and respect him. Eventually, a change of government came about in South Africa and Nelson was offered his freedom.

There is still a great deal to be done in South Africa to undo the evils of apartheid and make the black people there equal and free in the word and spirit of the law. Nelson Mandela is still working very hard to that end.

Amelia Earhart

Today, huge jet planes take people all over the world in just a few hours. When the aviation age was beginning, early in this century, brave pioneers flew tiny aeroplanes with single-propellor engines. It was their courage and love of adventure that paved the way for today's air travel.

A young American girl, Amelia Earhart, was not quite quite sure what she wanted to be but she knew what she liked to do - she liked to fly planes. But in the 1920s, aviation was young too, and there were few jobs in it for men let alone women.

Amelia went to college but interrupted her studies to help care for the wounded Canadian soldiers who were coming home from World War I. She learned to repair automobiles and she studied medicine. But always in the back of her mind was a desire to work in aviation.

It was luck that got Amelia her first big chance and pushed her to fame. In 1928, a wealthy woman named Mrs Guest wanted to be the first woman to cross the Atlantic Ocean in an aeroplane. She arranged for a pilot, Wilmer Stultz, and a flight mechanic, Louis Gordon, to take her from Newfoundland on Canada's east coast to England. They were to fly in a small aeroplane called the *Friendship*. At the last minute Mrs Guest decided not to go. Maybe it was the size of the tiny Fokker monoplane compared to the size of the ocean that gave her second thoughts. A substitute had to be found. Amelia Earhart was delighted to be asked.

Even though she was a qualified pilot, Amelia never had a turn at flying the *Friendship*. She only rode along as a passenger. But when the plane landed in Wales nearly twenty-one hours later, it was Amelia who was hailed as a hero. She wrote a book about her experiences on that flight.

However, Amelia always felt that she had not earned the fame showered on her for the trans-Atlantic crossing. It was Stultz the pilot who really did the work. She decided that she would be the first woman to fly across the Atlantic alone. She had always admired Charles Lindburgh, the first man to have done it.

She asked a pilot friend called Bernt Balchen to modify a small single-engine aeroplane for her so she could carry extra fuel for the journey. On the 20th of May 1932, Amelia took off from Newfoundland, bound for Paris. She was all alone above the vast Atlantic Ocean, doing what she loved to do most.

Amelia encountered numerous problems on the flight. The instrument that told her how high she was flying did not work properly. Ice accumulated on the wings, making the aeroplane heavier. The exhaust cracked and there was a leak in her reserve tank. Amelia knew she was not going to make it to Paris. Luckily for her, she found a safe landing place in Northern Ireland. She had been flying for thirteen-and-a-half hours. She was once again seen as a heroine.

Not content to be the first woman to fly the Atlantic solo, Amelia kept on flying and breaking records while she did.

In 1937 Amelia tried for another record, a bid that this time would prove fatal. She took off from Oakland in California in an attempt to be the first woman to fly solo all round the world. She crossed the United States, flew down the coast of Brazil, across the Atlantic, across Africa and across Asia. She made a final refuelling stop in New Guinea, near Australia, before setting out on the last dangerous leg of her round-the-world trip. She flew out over the Pacific Ocean and was never to be seen again.

No wreckage of her aeroplane was ever found. Amelia Earhart had disappeared.

Solidarity and Lech Walesa

Trade unions are organisations for workers. The officials of the union speak for the workers in discussions or disputes with the people who own the factories or other places of work. In communist countries the governments own the factories and run the trade unions. That means the workers don't have anyone to speak for them so they are not really fairly represented at all. That is the way it was in Poland after the Second World War when Lech Walesa was growing up.

During the war the Nazis had attempted to enslave or exterminate the Polish people just as they had the Jews. When the war ended, Poland then came under the domination of the Soviet Union. The country was in ruins and its people were terribly poor. Things did not get better under Soviet communism.

The Poles worked very hard to try to rebuild their country. Lech Walesa was one of the thousands of workers who toiled long hours in poor conditions for very little pay. Coal miners, for example, might work all day underground and only get one sausage for lunch.

Lech moved to Gdansk to a new job in a shipyard. There he became very aware of the hard lives all Poles were leading and he realised how unfair it was. Things might be getting better for the corrupt Communist Party bosses but the workers' lives stayed miserable. Lech's sense of justice and fair play was enraged. He began to speak out, sticking up for anyone who opposed the system.

Lech was not a politician or a public speaker. He was just an ordinary man who had been pushed far enough. His open, honest way of speaking gained him many followers. His fellow workers first and then those in other cities began to listen to and trust him. He led strikes and demonstrations. The Polish government, prodded by the Soviet Union, hit hard at the strikers. The demonstrators however, kept their promise of non-violent resistance. Out of the conflict grew a new union called Solidarity. Not only Polish workers believed in and supported Solidarity. All kinds of people around the world applauded Solidarity's fight for workers' rights and freedoms.

Lech Walesa and other Solidarity leaders were persecuted and imprisoned but they did not abandon their principles or the people who believed in them. The fight for Solidarity continued in the face of brutal government repression.

Finally, Lech was released from prison and allowed to go back to work as an ordinary citizen but the world had not forgotten that he was an extraordinary man. In 1983, Lech was awarded the Nobel Peace Prize. His long, non-violent campaign on behalf of the workers had been rewarded with the most prestigious recognition in the world. Lech's wife, Danuta, and their eldest son went to

Sweden in place of Lech to receive the prize because Lech was afraid his government wanted to be rid of him and would not let him come home to Poland if he went out of the country to accept the prize himself.

Lech continued his work with Solidarity and the government was forced to recognise him as a leader of the workers. There is no doubt that the founding of Solidarity helped to bring about the downfall of communism in Eastern Europe.

With the break up of the Soviet Union and the freeing of Poland from the Soviet Bloc, things moved quickly for the stocky little shipyard worker from Gdansk. He is now President of Poland.

The Captive University

We are very lucky to have schools in which pencils and paper and books are so plentiful we can take them for granted. But imagine living in a place where learning is forbidden and where there are no materials except what people can scrounge. These were the circumstances under which a secret university was started inside a Japanese prison camp in Burma during the Second World War.

A man named Frank Bell had been taken prisoner and sent to a Japanese camp where he was kept with many other Englishmen and Australians. The deprivation in Japanese camps was severe. The prisoners did not have enough to eat. They lived in inadequate buildings. They had poor medical attention and were forced to do very hard and dangerous work. Many of them died. But the deprivation they suffered was not just physical. They were also deprived of things like books that could have made them feel less isolated and given them something positive to think about during their imprisonment. In fact, the Japanese treatment of their prisoners was so severe that it went against the international rules for how prisoners should be treated. These rules were set out in the Geneva Conventions.

Frank Bell realised there were many men with him the camp who had particular skills and abilities they could teach to others, and that there were many who would like to learn. He decided to start a university right under the noses of the Japanese soldiers who guarded the camp. There were specific rules in the camp forbidding any teaching or learning to take place, so if they were caught their punishment would be solitary confinement or even death. The Japanese command wanted to be sure the prisoners had nothing to look forward to - nothing to give them any interest in the next day or the next week. They wanted a feeling of complete hopelessness to pervade the camp and the best way to do that was to keep the prisoners from thinking about the future. And learning something new gives hope for change. If you are studying something you find exciting and interesting, you look forward to the next lesson.

Frank Bell found many teachers among the prisoners and they set up courses in foreign languages, history, navigation, and even pig farming. Because the university was forbidden, it had to function in complete secrecy. The classes could not be

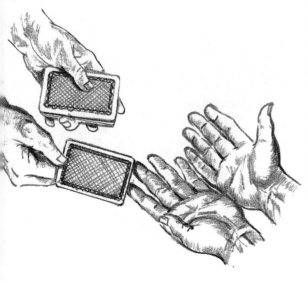

held with a teacher standing in front of a group of students and lecturing. One of the ways the prisoners found of holding classes was to sit in a circle and pretend to play cards while they were actually asking and answering questions about the subject being taught.

There was no equipment or supplies for the university. Paper and pencils had to be found. Every scrap of paper was precious. The students of the secret university wrote on any bit of paper they would find - the backs of envelopes from precious letters from home, soap wrappers, old newspapers, even cigarette papers. Of course, there was some competition for these as the men who smoked wanted them too. Frank Bell even managed to get enough tobacco papers to manufacture tiny text books. He assembled each one by hand, sewing and sticking the pages together and then making covers for them from scraps of cloth.

Because of the hardships and deprivations of life in the prison camp, many of the men died or became too ill to continue their studies. Despair also took its toll and many just gave up trying. But, by the time the war ended, a number of prisoners had earned degrees and Frank Bell awarded them hand-written diplomas.

When we are tempted to take school for granted, or when we think it is boring, it might be a very good idea to think of Frank Bell and his fellow prisoners. Learning was so important to them, they were willing to risk their lives for it.

Sadako Sasaki

Leukaemia is a kind of cancer of the blood. Doctors and scientists do not know all the causes of leukaemia but they have known for a long time that exposure to radiation from nuclear reactions can cause it. This was the way Sadako Sasaki got leukaemia.

Sadako was two years old when the United States dropped a nuclear bomb on the Japanese city of Hiroshima. They did it because they wanted to end the Second World War by forcing Japan to surrender. It was the most powerful bomb ever known. In an instant it killed thousands of people and completely destroyed the city.

But there was also an unseen, long-term effect. The deadly atomic radiation spread undetected for many miles. It spread throughout the the outskirts of the town where two-year-old Sadako lived. At the time there were no noticeable effects of the deadly rays. The bomb was dropped on the 6th August 1945 and it was not until five years later that Sadako showed any signs of illness. It took the doctors some time before they diagnosed that she was suffering from leukaemia, a result of the bomb's radiation.

She gradually became weaker and had to go into hospital. There were many other children there suffering from the same disease. They did not like their nasty-tasting medicine so, to persuade them to take it,

the nurses said they could use the empty medicine wrappers to make origami figures. Sadako knew the old Japanese folklore that if you made one thousand origami cranes you would be made well. She started to make these paper birds. Gradually the numbers increased: one hundred, two hundred, three hundred. When her school friends came to visit her they always wanted to know the new total.

Sadako hoped that other people would not have to suffer as she had done. As she finished each crane, she wrote the word 'Peace' on the wings, held it up and said, 'I send you to spread peace to the world'.

Although Sadako was a very determined girl she did not achieve her target. She gradually became weaker and when she died at the age of twelve she had only made 647 cranes. Her school friends were so impressed by her determination that they went to the hospital and together they made more cranes to bring the number up to the thousand. They then hung these one thousand cranes over her bed.

But that was not the end of the story. Sadako's bravery became well known all over Japan. People started to send money and more cranes. It was decided to use the money to build a monument in Peace Park, Hiroshima, in memory of Sadako and the others who had suffered in the same way.

The monument is an open-ended tower with a golden crane on top. It has now become a tradition for school children worldwide to visit the monument and to bring with them cranes to hang inside. This tradition still continues today, nearly fifty years after the bomb was dropped. Hopefully, it will be there for many years to come to remind people of the futility of war and make them more determined to work for peace.

Greed

Greedy people are never very popular. They don't make very good friends because they don't like sharing. They only think about themselves. They always grab first, trying to take the largest cake or that extra sweet. Often their greed can mean them missing out on more important things like friendship.

It is very difficult sometimes not to be greedy. It takes a lot of willpower to wait when your favourite cake is on the table. Will someone take it before you? It is hard to wait patiently until you are offered the plate.

Some children are so greedy that they even steal from their classmates. This is when greediness can lead to trouble. Quite often these children are not poor; they're not deprived. In fact, many of them have plenty of sweets or money of their own. They steal because they're greedy.

One of Aesop's Fables describes what can happen to greedy people.

The story tells of a dog who found a juicy bone. He was delighted and ran off to gnaw at it in a secluded place. He had to pass over a river. As he crossed the bridge he looked down into the water. There he saw a dog with a bone which looked twice as large as his. He was determined to have that one too. He opened his jaws and grabbed. To his dismay his own bone fell in the water and floated away. When the water became calm again he could still see the other dog but his bone had gone as well.

Because of his greed, the dog had allowed his own reflection to deceive him. Sometimes you can be so busy 'wanting' something else that you don't appreciate what you already have.

There is a story told about some people of the jungle who devised a very clever way of catching monkeys. They used the fact that the monkeys were greedy.

The people left heavy, narrow-necked jars where the monkeys could see them. They enticed the monkeys by placing some of their favourite nuts in the jars. The monkeys approached and slid their hands into the jar and grabbed the nuts. But when they tried to withdraw their hands they couldn't. Their clenched fists were too big. The monkeys wouldn't let go of the nuts even when they saw the people approaching to catch them.

Mahatma Ghandi was a kind and gentle man who was a leader in India, over forty years ago. This is what he said about greed: 'There is enough in the world for everyone's need, but not enough for everyone's greed. If everyone cared enough, and everyone shared enough, wouldn't everyone have enough?'

The Brave Vicar

Theodore Hardy had led a fairly ordinary life. He had been a school-teacher in Nottingham and later he became the vicar of a small parish in Cumbria. But he was to become the most decorated non-fighting person in the First World War.

When World War I broke out in 1914, Reverend Hardy applied to become a chaplain in the army. It was a job which would mean going to the war front to look after the soldiers. However, because he was fifty one years old, the army thought he was too old and refused to take him. He tried a few more times but each time they rejected him. He still felt he had a duty to help the troops and attended a first-aid course so he could qualify as a stretcher bearer, one of the men who helped to carry wounded soldiers off the battle field. Once again he was rejected, but finally, in 1916, the army relented and allowed him to become a chaplain.

During the next two years, he became a legend among the troops. Wherever the battle raged at its worst, Hardy would be there helping the wounded, comforting the dying and giving hope to the war-weary soldiers who had to keep fighting. Life in the trenches was terrible but Reverend Hardy shared all the hardships with the troops. He was a very modest man. He always announced his arrival by saying, 'It's only me,' when he climbed down into the trenches. He would only leave the war front when ordered to do so by high-ranking officers. He seemed to ignore the flying bullets and the exploding shells.

Reverend Hardy's bravery was recognised by everyone who saw him at work. He was awarded the Military Cross (the MC) and the Distinguished Service Order (the DSO). His most famous exploit earned him the Victoria Cross (the VC). He had joined his soldiers during an attack on an enemy position. As they were forced back, Hardy came across an injured soldier lying just beneath an enemy machine-gun position. He could not move the soldier on his own so he stayed with him, at the risk of his own life, from early morning until darkness fell. Then he crawled on his belly through the mud back to his own lines and persuaded a sergeant to go with him to carry the wounded soldier to safety.

Because of this act of courage and selflessness, he was awarded the Victoria Cross. The medal was presented to him by King George V on a special visit to the front lines. Because of his modesty, Hardy wanted to refuse the medal. He believed that when he went to the aid of the wounded soldier he had only done what any human being should have done. It was only when someone explained that such a refusal would be an insult to the King that he decided to accept it.

King George V became very worried for the safety of Hardy and in an attempt to persuade him to go back to England offered him the position of his personal chaplain. It was an honour most men would have readily accepted but Hardy politely refused. Hardy's bishop offered him a vicar's job back home in England at twice the usual salary but once again Hardy preferred to stay with the troops.

Sadly, just before the war ended, Reverend Hardy was shot by a sniper. As he was carried away, he said to the stretcher bearers, 'I'm sorry to be a nuisance.' This was typical of him. He thought very little about himself but he cared greatly for his fellow men.

Food

No living thing can survive without food. Getting food is the main concern of all animals, and human beings are no different in this respect. The history of mankind is closely tied to how people have fed themselves over thousands of years. In the very beginning, primitive people were hunters and gatherers. They ate what they could find or what they could kill. People lived in small groups and foraged for fruits, nuts, berries and edible leaves. They hunted in bands, killing game they would share with the group. They ate it raw until they discovered how to use fire to cook it. They then roasted it on spits and hot rocks around communal bonfires. After several thousand years they learned to keep animals that they could slaughter when they were needed. Still they wandered, for they had to follow the animals wherever they grazed. Then people discovered how to grow crops. These were grasses that yielded grain that could be made into porridge or ground to make flour for bread. This change in eating habits meant people had to stay in one place to look after their crops and so the wandering groups became villages of people. And still the main work of every day was providing food to sustain life. Ask your parents what things they spend the most money on and food will be very near the top of the list. People still work to get food today.

Because food was so important to life, it took a place of central importance in ceremonies and social occasions. There are many cultures in which a host provides lavishly for his guests. Some American Indian tribes had a gift-giving ceremony called Potlatch to which a chief invited people from miles around. He showered them with extravagant gifts and fed them at a seemingly endless banquet. On a smaller scale, a good Chinese host must provide food for his guest until the guest cannot eat any more. Whenever the guest finishes what is on his plate, more food must be provided. A good guest is one who knows to leave a tiny morsel as a signal that the host may stop providing food.

Many religions have ceremonies that are to do with food. Christians re-enact Christ's last supper by eating communion bread and drinking communion wine in church. And Christians say grace at table before eating to thank God for the food. Part of the Jewish celebration of Passover is a very special meal at which symbolic foods are eaten while the story of the first Passover is read. It is the most sacred night in the Jewish year. Many religions forbid the eating of certain foods. These are usually particular animals like pigs. More primitive religious celebrations often included the sacrifice of animals that would otherwise have been eaten. This symbolized people sharing with their gods and giving thanks for what they had.

We live in the industrialized part of the world where food is plentiful and where very few of us have to worry about where our next meal is coming from. We rush in from school and say, 'I'm starving! What's for tea?' We know there will *be* something for tea. And we are not really starving. But some people are. There are millions of our fellow human beings who have so little to eat that they are dying from hunger. In many countries there have been years of poor harvests, drought and wars. We have all seen pictures in magazines and on television of starving people who have so little flesh on their bones we wonder how they can stand up. Closer to home there are people who have no homes and no jobs. They live on the streets of our cities and they do not have enough to eat either. People have always had a tradition of sharing food. Even primitive people hunted in groups and shared the kill. Through the centuries families have shared food round the table at meal times. Extended families get together for holiday feasts. We are taught that all people are part of the family of humankind. This means we must try even harder to share what we have with people who have so much less than we have that they are dying.

Spiders

Do you know anyone who is afraid of spiders? Lots of people are. Ask someone who is afraid of them how many legs a spider has. Often a person who is afraid of them thinks they have more legs than they really do. Spiders have eight legs. They are not insects though people often think they are. They are arachnids and are more like crabs than like insects.

Spiders can be found all over the world and occur in a wide variety of sizes and shapes. They are carnivores. That means they eat other animals and it is this trait that makes them useful to us. Look in a spider's web some time and see what it has caught for its dinner. You will probably see an insect pest like a fly or a mosquito caught on the sticky strands of the web. If you are patient and observant you might see the spider wrap the dinner up for safe-keeping, or you might see it sucking the body juices from its prey.

The common garden or orb spider is a master architect. It constructs its web from sticky filament laid out in a careful spiral on the non-sticky spokes of web it has attached to the vegetation or, perhaps, a fence. The webbing material is produced within a spider's abdomen and is fed out by the spineretts at the tip of the abdomen. The sticky strand is for trapping prey and the non-sticky is for walking on. The spider can produce this silk very quickly. Try blowing a spider off your hand. Instead of falling, it abseils safely down on its thin

35

strand of web. Money spiders use their webs for travelling. In the autumn, they decorate the countryside with miles of fine filaments. You may see them glinting in the sun or rippling in the breeze. Many tiny spiders have been at work. Some have travelled miles, blown along with their little parachutes of web.

Maybe you will be observant enough to find a spider's egg newly hatched. The tiny new spiders cluster close to the empty egg case and look like pale dust. Slowly they fan out through the web. Tap the web very gently and watch them swarm toward the safety of the egg case.

Not all spiders spin webs. Some jump on their prey. Others can squirt sticky strands from their fangs to trap their prey. Some kinds of spiders build themselves lairs with tunnels of web for an entrance. There are even some that build themselves underground hides with trapdoors. They crouch below their doors and wait for something edible to walk by. Then they reach out and grab it. There are huge spiders that live in trees and eat birds. Even if you weren't afraid of the usual spider, you might find these a bit worrying. There are others almost too small to see.

Some people keep spiders as pets. Tarantulas are a favourite kind. They can be the size of your hand and are quite hairy and nicely coloured in rusts and browns. People who keep them for pets say they are interesting and affectionate.

There are lots of superstitions about spiders. Some people say it is bad luck to kill a spider or that it will bring rain. Finding a spider on your clothes is supposed to bring money or a letter. Finding one crawling on your body means good fortune will come to you. What must the spider think, looking out at you with its eight eyes? Is it good luck for a spider to find itself crawling on your body?

What a variety of spiders there are! And that's just spiders. The world is full of so many wonderful creatures that we should never run out of things to learn about.

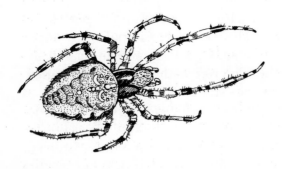

Alexander and Bucephalus

Philip, King of Macedonia, was buying horses. The magnificent animals were nervous as their grooms walked them past the King. His handsome, twelve-year-old son Alexander watched with interest. There were many horses suitable for Philip's mounted warriors and Philip was happy to pay the prices asked. There was a pause in the proceedings. Then accompanied by shouting and loud whinnying, a groom struggled into the arena trying to get control of a huge black stallion. The horse was nearly wild. His black mane and tail streamed in the breeze. His coal-black coat glistened in the sunlight. He tossed his broad head, pulling the groom off his feet. He kicked and tried to bite anyone in reach. Though it was a beautiful animal, Philip was sure it would be of no use in battle. A mounted warrior, riding bareback as they did, could not struggle with an unruly horse and fight well at the same time. He told the groom to take the animal away.

Alexander was dismayed. He could not bear to see such a wonderful horse wasted simply because there was no one capable of taming and riding him. Alexander's father heard his comments and asked Alexander if he thought he was horseman enough to do it himself. Philip was not fully prepared for Alexander's answer. After all, Alexander was only a boy. But Alexander said he wanted the stallion and so Philip agreed to buy the horse for him if he could ride it. Alexander accepted the challenge.

While the horse had cavorted before them, Alexander had been watching him carefully. He had not just looked and seen merely a beautiful and powerful horse. He had also observed the animal's behaviour and he had made a very useful discovery. The horse seemed to be afraid of his own shadow. Alexander took the halter from the groom who was happy to get clear of the stallion. Slowly but firmly Alexander turned the mighty animal to face the sun. That way he could not see his shadow which was cast behind him on the dusty ground. Carefully Alexander mounted and pulled the reins up to hold the horse still. The stallion's body was warm and strong. Alexander could feel the power at his command. When he felt in complete control, Alexander urged the stallion forward and broke into a gallop. The boy had earned his horse.

Alexander named the stallion Bucephalus which means 'head of a bull' because of his mighty, broad head. They were constant companions. No one but Alexander could ride Bucephalus and the horse would kneel to let Alexander mount.

In time, Alexander inherited his father's throne and he became Alexander the Great, one of the most powerful people in the world. He led his armies to victories over many enemies and captured lands from Greece to India. His prowess on the battlefield was legendary. And always in battle he sat astride his faithful Bucephalus. They would ride at the head of their army — beautiful black Bucephalus and Alexander with his helmet glinting in the sun, its white plumes flying. It must have thrilled even the enemy to see such a pair.

The trust that developed between the man and his horse lasted until Bucephalus died. Alexander's army was engaged in a tumultuous battle. Men and horses from both sides fell all around them. Suddenly Bucephalus stumbled, mortally wounded. It was a wound that would have killed any other horse where he stood. But Bucephalus turned from the battle and carried Alexander to a place of safety. As soon as Alexander was safely dismounted, faithful Bucephalus fell dead.

Fire

The discovery of fire and its uses was a great leap forward in the history of mankind. Early humans, called *Homo erectus*, probably discovered the use of fire by mistake. Perhaps lightning struck a tree and started a fire. How ever it was that humans discovered fire, they soon found many uses for it. We can only guess how long it was before they learned to make fire by using flints to create a spark. For a long time people probably carried smouldering firecoals with them to start new fires. If their fire went out, they would have to find it again or, more probably, steal it from another group of people. It is probable that these early people discovered the idea of cooking meat when they ate animals that had been killed by fire. Not only was cooked meat tastier but it was also easier to chew than raw meat.

In cold northern climates fire provided warmth. It was also used as a weapon. Animals were frightened of fire and could be kept away from encampments by bonfires kept burning all night. If a group of nomadic hunters came upon a cave that would make a good shelter, only to find it already occupied by an animal, they could drive the beast away using flaming torches. And once inside the dark cave, the fire provided them with light. People could not have made the beautiful cave paintings they did without the light of fires to see by.

Through the centuries people found more and more uses for fire. They believed it to be one of the four elements from which all the world was made. They learned to convert its heat into other forms of energy and used it to do many kinds of work. They found many kinds of fuel and learned to make more and more efficient fires.

They also learned how dangerous fire can be when it is out of control. Fire used as a weapon was indiscriminate. It could burn whole cities to the ground. Retreating armies would often burn everything in sight so there was nothing of value for the victorious to conquer.

Fire could cook your food and warm your house but if it was not used carefully, it could burn your house down and kill your family. There are many great fires in history. One of the biggest was the Great Fire of London in 1666. The ovens in the King's bakery in Pudding Lane in the City of London set the wooden building on fire. The wind was high and it took only a short time for more old wooden buildings

nearby to catch fire. Fire-fighting apparatus was still very primitive and there was no hope of controlling the blaze. People formed bucket brigades to try to save their homes. They stood in long lines from the River Thames to a burning building, handing full buckets along the line in one direction and empty ones back to be filled again. But it was of no more use than spitting on the blaze. King Charles II rode into the streets and directed the blowing up of houses to make spaces so the fire could not spread. But the wind blew burning embers about and when they landed they started fires in other places. Fire fighters with their small hand-pump engines made no progress against the conflagration. Mercifully, on the third day, the wind shifted, blowing the fire back on itself and it burned out. When the smoke cleared, 13,000 homes had been destroyed and 100,000 people were homeless.

Today, fire brigades have modern, very effective fire-fighting equipment and protective clothing that allow them to fight fires very effectively. It is a dangerous job. An important part of it is instructing people about fire safety and inspecting places where people gather to make sure there is little or no danger of a fire starting.

Fire-fighters risk their own lives to save the lives of others. Their first thought upon reaching the scene of a fire is to save anyone who might be in danger. They must enter smoke-filled buildings and climb ladders to help people to safety. Then they must direct their attention to containing and quelling the fire. Fire-fighters are some of the real heroes of our society.

Amnesty International

'When the first two hundred letters came the guards gave me back my clothes. Then the next two hundred letters came and the prison director came to see me. When the next pile of letters arrived, the director got in touch with his superior. The letters kept coming and coming: three thousand of them. The President was informed. The letters kept arriving and the President called me to his office for a man-to-man talk. He said: "How is it a trade union leader like you has so many friends all over the world?" He showed me an enormous box full of letters he had received and, when we parted, he gave them to me. I still have them.'

This is how Julio de Penez Valdar of the Dominican Republic described how an Amnesty International letter-writing campaign brought about his release from a dungeon where he had been imprisoned, naked, because he dared to speak out for his fellow workers against his government.

Amnesty International is an organisation of small groups of people all over the world who work for the release of political prisoners. Their main weapon is letter-writing campaigns. An AI group adopts a prisoner of conscience - that is, someone who has been imprisoned because of his or her political or religious beliefs. An AI-adopted political prisoner is never a person who has used or advocated the use of violence. It can be a person of any race, religion or political persuasion. Amnesty International is strictly non-political. The AI adoption group sets out to publicise the plight of their prisoner and to write as many letters as they can to the government holding the prisoner. The letters let the government know that people outside their country know what they are doing and that they are treating their people unfairly. The letters are always polite and to the point. AI wants to make things better for the prisoner, not worse. It uses the power of words to fight injustice.

Amnesty International was the brain child of one man. Peter Benenson was a lawyer in London in 1960 when he read a newspaper article about two young men in Portugal who had been imprisoned for seven years. They had not committed a crime. They had simply drunk a toast to 'Liberty' and government agents had taken offence and arrested them. Peter Benenson was furious. He wanted to do something. He talked to some of his friends and together they organised a campaign called 'Appeal for Amnesty, 1961'. They were able to get *The Observer* Sunday newspaper to back the idea and agree to cover the appeal. Other newspapers in other countries also were interested so the appeal was international from the start. An artist named Diana Redhouse designed a symbol for the appeal which is still the symbol for Amnesty International. It is a twist of barbed wire with a candle, the symbol of hope, burning inside it.

There were so many political prisoners around the world that the appeal needed to last for more than a year. So the appeal became Amnesty International and the work goes on today. AI is very careful to adopt prisoners from many different kinds of countries so no one can say that their groups are in favour of one kind of politics or another. This careful balance has made AI the most respected watchdog of human rights in the world.

There are many success stories of released prisoners, like the one at the beginning of this story. There are many AI groups all over the world engaged in letter-writing campaigns to get other people released. There are thousands more political prisoners in dungeons, in torture chambers, in prison cells all over the world whom no one has ever heard of. But Amnesty International is hard at work to bring justice to even the darkest, most dangerous corners and that is the promise of hope they offer to oppressed people everywhere.

Christopher Columbus

'In fourteen hundred and ninety-two, Columbus sailed the ocean blue!' American school-children sing this rhyme to help them remember one of the most important dates in their history. It was on 12th October 1492 that Christopher Columbus stepped ashore in the Americas.

Christopher Columbus lived in an age of discovery when people were learning a great deal about their world. The adventurer Marco Polo had journeyed overland to China about 200 years earlier and Europeans had come to appreciate things such as the spices that came from Asia. People no longer believed the world was flat and some of them reasoned that if the world was like a big ball, it would be possible to reach the lands that lay to the east by sailing westward. This would have been a very good idea if it hadn't been for the fact that the continents of North and South America were in the way. But no one in Europe knew that at the time. Christopher Columbus set out to sail to Japan, China and the East Indies, not to discover America. And, in fact, he was a little disappointed the way things turned out.

Columbus was a very capable navigator and sailor but he was not wealthy enough to buy and equip boats and hire the crews for his venture. He was sure that if could set sail he would find a shorter way than the land route to the rich lands of Asia and would be able to open up profitable trade routes. He appealed to the King of Portugal for help but was refused. Then Columbus turned to King Ferdinand and Queen Isabella of Spain for financial backing, promising them great riches in return for their investment. It took six years for him to get an answer. But Columbus was a very determined man. When the Spanish king and queen finally agreed to help him he set about preparing three boats for the journey. They were the *Niña*, the *Pinta* and the *Santa Maria*. By today's standards they were very small for ocean-going vessels. On the third of August 1492, the intrepid crews set sail westwards.

There had been explorers who had previously sailed as far into the Atlantic as the islands of the Azores but no further. So when Columbus's ships left the Azores they were sailing in uncharted waters. They had no idea how far they would have to go to see land again. They must have had wild ideas about sea monsters and other terrible fates that might befall them. But they trusted Columbus's judgement and were excited about the voyage. They had favourable winds and travelled fast with them. (These are now known as the trade winds.) They spent days sailing through the brown, floating seaweed of the Sargasso Sea. As the journey lengthened and all they saw in every direction was more water, they grew uneasy. On the 10th of October, they attempted to mutiny. They wanted to force Columbus to turn back. How could they know they were within a couple of days of reaching land? Luckily, Columbus was able to calm their fears and talk them into sailing further on.

Very early on the morning of the 12th of October, they sighted land by moonlight. Imagine the joy and relief of the crew! They had been at sea for more than two months, not knowing if they would ever see land again. They laughed with relief and sang hymns in thanks.

The next day they were able to anchor and send a party ashore. Columbus thought he had arrived in Japan. But it was not Japan. It was an island whose inhabitants called it Iguana Island, in the Caribbean Sea. Columbus renamed it San Salvador. Columbus and his crews found the native population peaceful and the place was not unpleasant. But Columbus was disappointed. He had set out to sail to Asia and he had come upon this unknown land. He thought he had failed.

He continued to search, certain he would find Japan somewhere among the many islands but, of course, he did not. He did not appreciate what an enormously important discovery he had made. He had to go home to King Ferdinand and Queen Isabella without the treasure he had promised. But he had led the way for other Spanish sailors who sought riches in the lands of the Americas and claimed much of the 'New World' for Spain.

Many intrepid explorers would follow after Columbus, looking for thousands of miles up and down the coasts of North and South America, seeking, like him, for a way through to Asia. But it would be a long time before anyone was able to finally find the western sea route to Asia by sailing around the southern tip of South America and into the Pacific Ocean.

Tea's Made!

Ahh. Tea. A chance to sit down, relax and have a refreshing cup of tea.

This happens every day in millions of homes and places of work. People take tea breaks. But how did we come to drink tea and where does it come from?

Tea is the youngest, tenderest leaves of the tea plant. Tea needs a frost-free climate but likes cool air. It is on mountainsides in the tropical areas of the world that tea grows best. Some of the main tea-producing countries are India, China, Sri Lanka and Japan.

The Chinese were the first to drink tea and that started about 3,000 years ago. As people travelled more to other lands, they took their ideas with them and the Chinese took the idea of tea drinking with them to Japan and India. The Japanese adopted the drinking of tea and attached great ceremony to the sharing of tea between hostess and guests. This Japanese tea ceremony is still practiced in Japan. It is very ritualistic and takes a long time to go through. It is not the way to get a cup of tea in a hurry.

Over 300 years ago, when overland trade routes began to open, tea found its way to Europe. It was first drunk in England about 1650. It was very expensive and only very wealthy people could afford it. Tea houses catered for the new taste in exotic drinks, brewing it in small pots and serving it in small cups because of its cost.

About 150 years ago tea clippers began to carry tea from Asia to Europe. These were large but very fast sailing ships. They had several masts and carried many sails. It took about a hundred days for these ships to make the voyage and clipper ship captains often engaged in races to see who could get the tea to Europe first.

As more and more tea came onto the market, its price went down and ordinary people could afford to drink it. Soon it was common in most homes. It was kept fresh in air-tight tins called caddies and brewed in large pots so everyone in the family could enjoy it. Men often took cold tea to work in bottles to give them a refreshing drink with their packed lunches. About 1825, afternoon tea became a tradition and then bread and butter or cakes were added to make it a small meal. Now, in many homes, it is the evening meal.

Put some tea into a spoon and look at it closely. It doesn't resemble lush green leaves at all. But that is how it started out. Tea is grown on plantations where there are rows and rows of tea bushes about a metre or more high. Tea is really a tree and could grow to be 10 metres or more tall if allowed to. But that would make the young shoots very hard to pick so the plants are pruned and trained to grow only as high as the pickers can reach.

Tea is a labour-intensive crop. This means lots of people have to work very hard to raise, harvest and process it. Most tea pickers are women. They live in countries where the standard of living is low and people do not earn much money. The tea pickers strap big baskets to their backs and pick over the tea bushes, taking only the buds and the first two leaves. They get to be very good at it and can pick quickly, filling their baskets, emptying them and filling them again. It is very hard work. The tea is then taken to the factory. In some areas people carry the enormous sacks of freshly picked tea on their heads. At the factory the tea undergoes several processes. It must be dried and rolled to take out remaining juices. Then, if it is to be green tea, it is scorched. If it is to be black tea, the kind most of us drink, it is fermented for a few hours. During this time it turns from green to brown. Then it is put into the firing machine and dried completely. After this is done you would recognise it as tea. The tea must be packed into tea chests and shipped all over the world where, at tea auctions, the big tea companies buy what they need. They box it under their own labels and send it out to the shops.

The next time you have a cup of tea, you might stop to think about how many people worked to get it to your lips. Ahhh, tea!

Living with Asthma

Put your hands on your lower chest and feel your ribs rise and fall as you breathe. Your breathing muscles move to let air into your lungs and then they move again to squeeze the air out. You might hear a soft rushing of air in your nose or mouth. It happens all day, every day without you thinking about it. It is involuntary movement. Your body does it for you without you telling it to. But for some people, illnesses make breathing difficult, and one of them is asthma.

When you breathe in, the air goes down a big tube called your trachea which separates into two and goes into your right and left lungs. These tubes branch, much like a tree, into smaller and smaller tubes, ending finally in air sacs called alveoli. From these sacs, the oxygen in the air goes into your blood and is carried all around your body. Oxygen combines with nutrients from food to give you energy. Then the blood carries the waste product, a gas called carbon dioxide, to your lungs and you breathe it out. In, out, in, out, all day and all night. You do it without thinking. But people with asthma sometimes have difficulty breathing and if they are having a bad attack, they can think about nothing else. It can be very frightening not being able to breathe easily. If you have asthma, or have a friend who has, you will know how unpleasant it can be.

There are different reasons people get asthma but the symptoms are similar. Some people only get asthma when they exercise and get breathless. This is called exercise asthma and is usually more troublesome when the air is cold and dry. There is also chronic asthma, which means being a bit out of breath all the time. This usually affects older people. Some people are allergic to certain things in the air or in food. If they come into contact with these allergens, the tubes in their lungs constrict and become smaller so air has a hard time getting through. Their lungs also produce a thick mucus. Sometimes their breathing whistles or sounds wheezy. They might cough. Asthma sufferers might pull their shoulders up in an effort to get more air. It is very tiring working so hard to breathe. Sometimes they might feel resentful or unhappy about having asthma.

Asthma seems to be increasing, especially among children. Doctors and scientists are very concerned about this. Some people think it is a result of the increasing amount of air pollution. Asthma is not contagious. You cannot catch it from someone. Some children with asthma will outgrow it when they are teenagers. Other people will not get it until they are older. Most people will never have asthma at all.

For asthma sufferers there are many different kinds of medicines to help them cope with their illness. They learn to help themselves so they can live a normal life. The most important thing someone with asthma can do is stay generally healthy. A head cold can bring on an attack of asthma. They try to avoid the allergens that

cause them difficulty. They learn to measure how much air they are breathing, because this helps them predict when a bad attack might begin. To do this they blow into a tube that measures how hard they can blow out. The greatest amount of pressure they can exert with an exhaled breath is called their peak flow. If peak flow is very poor it might mean a bad attack is about to begin and they can see a doctor or go to the hospital. There are different ways of taking medication for asthma. Perhaps you know someone who uses an inhaler for drawing medication deep into their lungs. There are also machines called nebulisers that vaporise the medication. This means it breaks it up into very tiny droplets and mixes it with the air. The asthma patient is then able to breathe air with the medicine in it for a longer period of time than the one or two puffs they get with the inhaler. There are also tablets people can take. As with most illnesses, the most important thing a person with asthma can do is learn to manage it and live a normal life. It can be very worrying for people who live with an asthma sufferer, but with the help of doctors and medication, they can make life easier for the patient. You can help your friends who have asthma by being understanding and at the same time, treating them like everyone else.

Festivals of Light

In late October, piles of waste wood and garden rubbish begin to appear in fields and gardens all over the country. People are preparing for Guy Fawkes Night. The evenings get darker earlier and the nights are colder. The thought of a bright, warm bonfire is very appealing. Guy Fawkes Night is only one of many celebrations in which people light the night and scare away the darkness for a little while. Halloween, with jack 'o lanterns and pumpkins lit by candles, is another celebration in which we take light into the darkness.

There are festivals of light in many religions. During the four weeks leading up to Christmas we light Advent candles. At the Christingle Service we symbolise Christ as the Light of the World with a candle in an orange. We put lights on our Christmas trees. In paintings of the Holy Family, a halo of light round their heads symbolises their divinity and their connection with God. During Lent, churches are dark. There are no candles lit until very early on Easter morning. Catholics light the special Easter candle from a bonfire burning outside the church. That candle is used to light all the other candles as the people sing the words 'Lumen Christi'. This means 'Light of Christ' in Latin. The coming of light back into the church symbolises the resurrection of Christ from the dead.

Judaism has a festival of light called Chanuka. It is around the same time as Christmas and is celebrated with candles. Jewish households have a special candle-holder called a menorah. It holds eight candles and one for lighting the others. The celebration commemorates a return of light to the Jews' holiest temple in Jerusalem after they defeated the Syrians over two thousand years ago. On the first night of Chanuka one candle is lit. Each night after that, one more candle is lit until on the last night all eight are lit.

Hindus and Sikhs celebrate Diwali which means 'cluster of lights'. They place diva lamps outside their houses. It is a re-enactment of how, many hundreds of years ago, their ancestors did the same thing to light the way and guide their favourite Prince Rama and his wife Sita home to safety after a battle.

In Japan people celebrate the festival of Bon. This is a time when they believe the spirits of the dead return for an annual visit amongst the living. People make special visits to cemeteries and remember their

ancestors who have passed away. Special dances are performed in the streets and paper lanterns are lit to welcome the spirits. Later, at the end of the Bon festival, these lanterns are set adrift on the rivers. They carry the visiting spirits back to the afterlife. The most exciting part of Bon takes place on a mountain just outside the city of Kyoto. It is called the Okuribi. The Okuribi are very special bonfires made in the shapes of the Chinese writing used in Japan. There is a different word shape on each of five locations around the mountain. Before the start of the festival, stacks of logs and pine needles are built on stone hearths in lines to form the shapes. Each of them is set alight in turn and thousands of people on all sides of the mountain can see the fiery shapes from miles away. It is very exciting!

The people of the world have many different ways of worshipping and celebrating but we all share some important ideas about celebrating our festivals: the bringing of light is important to us all.

A Change of Heart

John Newton was born in 1725, the son of a ship's captain. His father was very strict with him but his mother was gentle and kind. She taught him to love God, and as a young child John attended church regularly. Unfortunately, when he was seven, his mother died. His father could not look after such a young child at sea so he was sent to boarding school. He was so badly treated there that four years later, at the age of eleven, he ran way and went to sea as a cabin boy on a merchant ship.

Life was hard on board ship but became even worse when, a few years later, he was captured by the 'press gang' and forced to join the Royal Navy. Conditions in the navy were so bad that no one wanted to join. It was the job of the 'press gang' to find a regular supply of men, capture them and make them unwilling sailors. John decided that his life had been so hard, so full of troubles, that there could not possibly be a God. He denied God's existence and swore never again to read the Bible, or even enter a church.

To escape from the horrors of serving in the navy, John applied for a transfer to a 'slave ship'. His request was granted and life became a little easier for him. In later life, however, he was ashamed of the part he played in the slave trade. Africans were captured and transported by ship, halfway round the world, to be sold as slaves to work on the cotton plantations in the southern states of America. So many Africans were packed into the ships that many died on the journey. On some ships, the captives were hand-cuffed to the lower decks, never seeing daylight during the long journey.

John Newton had sunk as low as it is possible for a man to sink. But it was on one of these trips that his life was completely changed. By chance, he picked up a book called *An Imitation of Christ* and he glanced idly through it. The words seemed to jump out at him. As he read, they made him realise what a dreadful life he had been leading and that somehow he must strive to change it. That same night a violent storm arose. The small sailing ship was tossed about on the mountainous waves and everyone, including John, was convinced they were doomed to die. Then suddenly, at the height of the storm, a feeling of peace came over him. Despite the ferocity of the storm he knew he was going to be safe. He felt that God was protecting him and so no harm could possibly come to him.

By morning the weather had changed - and so had John Newton. As soon as it was possible he left the ship and started living a new life. He forgot his previous vow that he would never read the Bible or enter a church again. His experience at sea had convinced him that God did exist. He knew it was God's love and protection which had saved him. He wrote about his conversion in his famous hymn, *Amazing Grace*. The first verse of which reads:

'Amazing Grace, how sweet the sound
That saved a wretch like me.

I once was lost, but now am found,
Was blind, but now I see.'

The 'wretch' spent the rest of his life serving God. In 1761 he was ordained as a priest. Later, he helped William Wilberforce in his attempts to abolish the slave trade. He will probably be remembered forever for the hymns he wrote. They are still sung, more than 180 years after his death.

The God-King

Tibetan Buddhists believe that after their spiritual leader dies, he is reborn. They believe he has been reborn thirteen times and that his soul now dwells in Tenzin Gyatso, the present Dali Lama - the God-King. He is the fourteenth Dali Lama. His name means Holder of the Faith and Ocean of Wisdom.

When the thirteenth Dali Lama died, the search began for the child into whom his soul would be reborn. The Dali Lama had died facing northeast so the monks who would find the next Dali Lama went off in that direction to search. They found their way to a village near a monastery for they had heard of a boy there who had been born at the right time, in the right year. He might be the boy who had the soul of the dead Dali Lama. Pretending to be ordinary travellers, the group of monks visited the peasant family and their child. When the monks met the little boy, whose name then was Lhamo Dhondrub, he astounded them by knowing many things about the dead Dali Lama. When Lhamo touched a string of beads that had belonged to the Dali Lama and said, 'These are mine,' the monks were hopeful, but still not convinced. There were many other tests to be done before they could be sure the boy was the new incarnation of the Dali Lama. Lhamo passed all the tests, was renamed Tenzin Gyatso and declared to be the four-teenth Dali Lama. He was five years old.

The new God-King was taken to live in the Potala. This was an immense palace, thirteen stories high with one thousand rooms, that was perched on a hillside overlooking the city of Lasa. Then began many years of study under the watchful eyes of the monks. They trained the boy and as he grew into a young man he also grew in wisdom and spirituality. He was loved and worshipped by his people as both God and King.

Tibet occupies a strip of mountainous land between India and China. These two countries were enemies and so Tibet found itself caught between warring giants. The Chinese felt they must occupy Tibet in order to guard the frontier with India. In about 1950, when Tenzin Gyatso was still a young man, the Chinese entered Tibet. At

51

first, the relationship between the Tibetans and the Chinese was fairly friendly. The Tibetans were allowed to carry on their traditions much as before. But things were destined to change. Chinese people began to move into Tibet in large numbers and there was pressure on the Tibetans to give up their traditional culture and religion and become like the Chinese. The Tibetans refused and rose against the Chinese. The revolt was cruelly put down. The Dali Lama and the leaders of the revolt had to escape over the Himalayan Mountains on horseback to safety in India.

They were joined by thousands of their countrymen. Their country was taken over by the Chinese. The Tibetan monasteries were stripped and burned. Many of the Tibetans who were left behind were killed, imprisoned or forced to move to other parts of China. The Chinese tried to obliterate the Tibetan culture.

But the Dali Lama and the people who escaped with him reached safety. They still live outside their country in refugee camps and foreign countries around the world. Because their spiritual leader - their God-King, their Dali Lama - is alive and still actively leads them, they feel all is not lost. But they long to go home to their own homeland, to Tibet.

The Mayans

About 3000 years before Christ, a civilisation was beginning to take shape in the rainforests of Central America. People moved down out of the mountains into the valleys to clear areas of the forest along the rivers. They brought maize seed with them to plant in the areas they cleared. The first settlements were along the rivers because the rainforests were so thick that it was impossible to travel through them. The only way to get from one settlement to another was by boat.

The Mayans were short, stocky people with straight, dark hair and slanted eyes. The Indians of Central America still have these characteristics today.

The early Mayans had to work very hard to clear the land. They had only simple tools which they could make themselves from stone and wood. The farms they made were small and they grew just enough to feed themselves. They had to fertilise the poor soil with ash from burning the trees they felled. The houses they built were made of tree trunks, branches and leaves. They usually had stone foundations to keep them out of the mud. The Mayans had to contend with wild animals like jaguars and with snakes and spiders. There were diseases and parasites that sickened and killed many of them.

In the beginning, the society that developed treated everyone alike. The chiefs were expected to do the same kind of work everyone else did. Then different crops were introduced, land became more valuable and squabbles about ownership were more frequent. A class of people developed who sorted out these squabbles. They came to be respected priests and they had a great deal of power. The religion of the Mayans was based on the world as they knew it. They worshipped gods who were like the animals of the rain forests.

As the culture and religion developed, the Mayans built bigger and better buildings. They learned to cut stone blocks and they used them to build huge, stepped pyramids. Many of these still stand today, hidden deep in the forests of Central America. They carved the faces of their animal gods to decorate the pyramids. They sacrificed animals on special stone altars on the tops of the pyramids as part of their worship.

The Mayans' ideas of what made a person beautiful seem unusual to us. Some of them distorted the shapes of their skulls. Some filed their teeth to points. Others embedded precious jewels in their skin.

As their culture developed, Mayans became interested in mathematics and astronomy. They observed the movements of the sun and the moon and so were able to develop a calendar much like the one we use today. They used this to help predict when their harvests would be. Mayan mathematicians devised a complex number system and were probably the first people to use the idea of zero.

The Mayans enjoyed sport and it was a very important part of their lives. They invented complex ball games and hundreds of spectators could watch from stepped terraces around the playing field.

When the Mayan civilisation was at its peak, it was a network of flourishing cities. These cities had pyramids and temples, market places and canals. Much of what had been jungle had been turned into vast plazas paved with stone slabs. Nobles and priests lived in fine stone villas.

But suddenly, for reasons no one can be sure of, the Mayan civilisation began to go into decline. The rainforest began to take over again. Slowly, it grew back over the plazas and fine houses. It crept over the palaces and pyramids until they were almost hidden from view. Even today, many have not yet been discovered, and are there, somewhere in the jungles, buried beneath the coverings of trees and creepers.

Off to a slow start

Eugene Oravitch, a young American boy, found life very difficult, especially when it came to school work. Words were very hard to understand, numbers were a mystery to him and his clumsiness made painting and model making almost impossible. In fact, there was nothing that he could really do well and he felt he was one of the world's biggest no-hopers.

One day, when he had just started secondary school, the PE master told the class that they were going to the running track to practice athletics. All the children were excited, except for poor Eugene. He knew that he would come last in everything and everyone would see how poor an athlete he was.

Sure enough, when the class lined up for the 100 metres sprint he hung back, but there was no escape. His turn came and when the others in his race sprinted away he was struggling well behind, puffing and panting. When he reached the finish he was red in the face from fatigue and embarrassment. It was just the same in the 400 metres, the long jump and, worst of all, the hurdles which he proceeded to knock down on his slow progress to the finishing line.

The teacher then announced that they were going to have their first attempt at throwing the javelin. There were cries of 'Don't let Oravitch have a go, sir. He'll either stab his own foot or spear somebody.'

Everyone tried, though no-one had much success, then, last of all, it was Eugene's turn. Reluctantly he picked up the javelin. As soon as he touched it, he felt a strange feeling in his arm. It seemed as though it was meant to be part of him.

Grasping the missile he staggered up the runway, drew back his arm and before he fell over, released it with a strong movement. The javelin flew through the air like Concorde taking off. On and on it went, metres past the previous longest throw and

landed gracefully a long way from his astounded classmates. There was a stunned silence, then everybody started cheering. 'Let him have another go, sir. It might have been a fluke,' they suggested. 'OK, Oravitch. Let's see you do it again,' said the PE master.

Eugene picked up another javelin, ran more confidently and heaved it even further. How pleased he was. Now there *was* something he could do better than anyone in his class. His face creased into a broad grin and he felt twice as tall.

It was obvious that he had this one special talent and he began to go regularly for extra coaching. Because he had now succeeded in something his other school work began to improve and eventually he was awarded a sporting scholarship to a university. He soon became the Inter-University Champion of the USA and there was confidence that he would become the next Olympic Gold medalist.

Then tragedy struck. Shortly before the team were ready to leave for the Olympic Games, Eugene was going through a training routine. As he was throwing the javelin he felt a sharp pain in his right shoulder and his arm fell limply to his side. Obviously, something was really wrong. His coach ran to his side, examined him and quickly took him to see a doctor. Tests followed and he was dismayed to learn that he had badly damaged his arm and he would never again be able to throw a javelin great distances. The only thing at which he excelled had been taken away from him. 'What could I do now?' he thought, as the Olympic team flew off and he was left to his misery. Poor Eugene!

Now, it so happened that his room-mate at university was very interested in acting. He had a starring part in the college play. One day, not long after Eugene's injury, his friend asked him if he would help him to learn his lines. Eugene sat miserably on his bed, knowing that his poor reading ability wouldn't be of much use, but his friend insisted. Reluctantly, he picked up the script and when he looked at the words something wonderful happened. The sensation he felt was just like the one he had experienced before when he picked up the javelin. Perhaps this was something else he would be able to do. He really enjoyed playing the parts in the play, while helping his friend. He was encouraged to join the Drama Group. Soon he was invited to take part himself and his new life as an actor had begun.

Eugene Oravitch was an unsuitable name for a TV and film actor so he changed it to Michael Landon. He had parts in several films before playing Little Joe in *Bonanza* and then he acted in and produced *Little House on the Prairie*. His last work on television was his production of the series *Highway to Heaven* and he died whilst still a young man early in 1992.

Through finding out that he *did* have talents, the man who had thought of himself as the world's biggest no-hoper had eventually brought pleasure to millions around the world.

Modern-Day Nomads

Most of the people you know probably live in houses, but this is not so for everyone. In recent years, more and more people have taken to living on the streets in big cities. Many of them are young people who for some reason have left home. Others are people who no longer have enough money to keep paying a mortgage on a house or rent for a flat. There are other homeless urban dwellers who have taken to the road in old buses and vans. They call themselves New Age Travellers. They go from place to place and camp in large gatherings with like-minded people. In some places they have made themselves unwelcome because some of them do damage to other peoples' property.

There is, however, another group of travelling people whose ancestors have been travelling for over a thousand years. They are the Gypsies. Real Gypsies are descended from a nomadic band of people who originated in India. Some of them moved slowly into what is now Iran. It was then called Persia. Then they spread through Eastern Europe and it was from the country of Romania that they got the name Romany Gypsies. They moved across Europe and the first Gypsies made their way to England about four hundred years ago.

True Gypsies are fiercely proud of their heritage. They have their own traditions and language, and Gypsy families can trace their lineage back many generations.

Though many Gypsies now live in houses, some still follow the traditional nomadic existence, either in modern caravans or horse-drawn Gypsy wagons. Even those who do live in houses make trips in true Gypsy style. There are particular gatherings which they like to attend each year, such as horse fairs in the Cumberland hills.

Whether they travel in modern caravans or old-fashioned wagons, Gypsies keep their homes on the road in pristine condition. They paint and polish them until everything is sparkling.

A traditional Gypsy wagon is a rolling work of art. It is painted with decorations in bright colours both inside and out. The bowed roof makes it unmistakable when on the road or parked on a grassy verge. Though the wagon is small it has everything a Gypsy family might need. There is a large bunk under which there is a special cupboard bed for the children. They can crawl in and close the doors behind them to make a cosy sleeping compartment. There is crockery and cutlery and even a stove for cooking. But much of the cooking can be done over an open fire out of doors.

Gypsies know a great deal about horses and they especially like black and white or brown and white patched or spotted ones. A Gypsy wagon usually has one horse pulling it and another tethered to the side, walking along. When the wagon approaches the bottom of a steep hill, the driver can hitch up the second horse to help with the pulling. When the wagon stops for the night, the horses are tethered nearby to graze.

Traditionally, Gypsies kept a special breed of dog called a lurcher. This was bred by crossing collies and greyhounds. It was a hunting dog and it would scour the countryside along the route for small game which it carried to the wagon for the Gypsy family to cook and eat.

Many people associated Gypsies with metal work and they are often confused with tinkers, who are of Irish descent. French Gypsies are known for their music and Spanish Gypsies for their dancing.

The next time you are sitting at home in your living-room you might like to stop and think what your life would be like at that moment if you were a Romany Gypsy pursuing a traditional Gypsy way of life.

People Underground

The first dwelling place human beings had was probably a cave. They might have had to turn out wild animals which had been living there. It provided them with shelter and safety.

Some people still live underground. In one part of China, people dig their houses out of the soil. They dig a deep, square hole for a central courtyard that they leave open to the sky. It has a staircase for access to ground level. At each side of the square they carve a room into the earth. Windows and doors open onto the courtyard and give plenty of light. The earth provides a good roof and insulation.

The cliff-dwelling Indians of the south-western United States carved whole settlements housing hundreds of people out of the red sandstone cliffs of the area. Many are still there, clinging to their precarious sites.

Some architects and builders in the western world today are very interested in the possibility of putting not just single houses but whole cities underground. They believe it is ecologically sound to do this because such buildings would be very energy-efficient. With the use of modern materials, underground dwellings can be completely isolated from damp and would suffer much less wear and damage from weathering. There are now kinds of lighting that exactly emulate natural sunlight.

And not only homes could be built underground but roads, parks and commercial buildings as well.

People may find the idea of living underground a bit strange but many of us are fascinated by caves and the mysteries they hold. Many people engage in the sport of caving or spelunking and spend exciting hours exploring underground. They are careful to take every precaution so their adventures do not end in tragedy. They have special clothes and equipment. They must take their own light with them down into the darkness.

There are numerous jobs that take people underground. Mining is one of them. In the last century there were thousands of children in Britain who spent all their days in the dark and dangerous coal mines, doing work to help miners extract the all-important coal that kept British industry going. There are also some very different kinds of work that are carried out underground. Wines are aged in cellars and mushrooms grown in them because they prefer dark, cool conditions.

Many of the world's big cities have underground railways that carry people through miles of tunnels below the city streets. There are many people who work in those tunnels doing jobs such as maintaining and repairing the track, driving trains, selling tickets and cleaning. Some stations, such as those on the Moscow underground, are like huge rooms in a palace and have marble walls and chandeliers. Others are simply functional. The London Underground was the first in the world and now it is a vast network of tunnels that go under and over each other at different depths under a great city. And these are only part of a labyrinth of tunnels of different diameters which carry such things as water, sewage, and telephone and electricity cables. Underground train travel is much faster than surface travel because there are few traffic problems with the electric trains speeding through the tunnels and large tubes. During the Second World War, Londoners used the underground stations to shelter from air raids.

People have often gone underground for safety and survival. The storm shelters of the tornado belt in the great plains of the United States are deep holes with covers over them. When one of the terrifying twisters approaches people can quickly escape into the shelters. In Britain, during World War Two, people dug bomb shelters in their gardens. Many were only trenches with earth piled over the top but they still gave more protection than buildings. The shelters had beds and places to sit where people waited out the air raids. During the 1970s and 1980s, when communist countries and western nations threatened each other with nuclear war, many people in the United States dug what were called fallout shelters. These were concrete-lined holes deep in the ground. People thought they would be safe there from the nuclear fallout if an atomic bomb were to be exploded. Many were kitted out with all the comforts of home and had vast supplies of food and water. In some, people kept weapons, for use not against the enemy but against their neighbours who had not dug their own fallout shelters and who might want to share their precious

food and water. Fortunately, these fallout shelters have never had to be used. Some governments have vast underground shelters in secret places where the country's leaders can go in case of war. In theory, they would continue to run the country and wage war from these bunkers. One of the largest networks of this kind is under the city of Bejing in China. After the communist revolution, the Chinese leaders were so afraid of being attacked by western countries that they dug miles and miles of tunnels connecting many large rooms beneath Bejing. There was enough room underground for all the people of Bejing in case of attack.

Perhaps in the next century people will be able to stop thinking about hiding underground from attack and think about expanding their growing cities downward into the ground. You might be able to look out over a city and see only the top layer. Or perhaps you will see only rolling hills, fields and forests. The busy metropolis might be completely hidden underground leaving the countryside on its roof for growing food and for recreation.

The Potato

The humble potato has had quite a history and it has made history, too. The potato was first discovered by Europeans when they found their way to South America during the Age of Discovery in the 16th century. Sir Walter Raleigh brought the potato to England from the New World and gave Queen Elizabeth I a plant for the royal gardens. Because of its adaptability, the potato became a popular, staple diet and many poor people depended upon it for food. During the 19th century, a terrible disease called blight attacked the potato crops and caused them to fail for several years. There was widespread famine because poor people who ate lots of potatoes had no food. Many of them decided to leave their homes and emigrate to America. Many of the people who went were from Ireland. There are many Irish Americans today who can trace their families back to people who fled during the great potato famine.

Potatoes don't just fill you up, they are also good for you. They are rich in vitamins, carbohydrate and fibre. There are lots of different kinds of potatoes, grown in different kinds of soil and for different kinds of cooking.

Lovely big potatoes are grown especially for baking, and small new potatoes are delicious when they are boiled.

One way we like to eat potatoes is as crisps. The crisps we eat today are made almost entirely by machine from potatoes that have been carefully aged. Then they are put into a potato-peeling machine that works like sandpaper, bouncing the potatoes around and around, rubbing and wearing the skin off them. They are very thinly sliced by a machine, then they are fried in deep fat. When the slices come out of the fat they are crisp and golden. Then they get salted or flavoured and packaged. When you open a packet of crisps you have a pretty good idea of what to expect.

But the first man to eat them had no idea what he was getting. And the first man to make them had no idea what an important thing he was doing. He invented crisps almost by accident about a hundred years ago. The man responsible for inventing crisps, or potato chips as they are known in his country, was an American. In fact, he was American Indian from a tribe called Adirondack. The man's name was George Crum and he was the head chef in a fine hotel where wealthy people liked to eat. One day a customer came in who had recently been to Paris in France. This customer thought he knew a thing or two about how food should be cooked and when his french fried potatoes arrived he thought they were too soft and sent them back to Chef Crum in the kitchen. The chef was a little put out and prepared some more potatoes, cooking them a little longer. Still the man complained that the potatoes were not crispy enough. Chef Crum was furious. He was proud of his well-deserved reputation as a very good chef and he was not about to let an overly fussy customer get the better of him. Chef Crum sliced some potatoes wafer-thin. He fried them in very hot fat until they were

crisp all the way through. He served them to the man as if to say: 'You want 'em crispy? You got 'em crispy!' To George Crum's surprise, the man liked them!

It wasn't long before people came to the hotel especially to get Chef Crum's lovely crispy fried potatoes.

Sun Power

There has been a lot of talk recently about solar power. More and more people are using solar cells to make electricity. The sun's light is collected in special trays that change it into electrical energy. It is a very good way to make use of the sun's energy. But we use the sun's energy in other ways for everything we do every day.

Green plants depend on sunlight to live and grow. We eat green plants or we eat animals that eat green plants. There would be no egg and chips without the sun. The hen that laid the egg ate grain that came from a green plant. The potatoes that became the chips grew on a green plant. And what about the Sunday roast? When it was still walking around, it was an animal that ate green plants. No sun would mean no green plants. No green plants would mean no food. No food means no energy to stay alive.

Are you breathing? You can thank the sun for that, too. As green plants grow, they give off oxygen. Oxygen is the gas we take in when we breathe. So without the special relationship between the sun and green plants we would have no oxygen to breathe. This is one of the main reasons people are so worried about the millions of trees that are being cut down in forests all over the world. Trees make fresh air.

What about the electricity that does so much work for us? Electricity generators must use some form of energy to turn the turbines that make the electricity. If it is a coal- or gas-burning generator, the fuel was once green plants. Reserves of coal and gas and petroleum buried deep under the ground or sea bed are the remains of green plants or animals that were buried millions of years ago. So you've also got the sun to thank for that.

Some electricity is produced when fast-running water turns turbines. This kind of power generator is called hydroelectric. Where does the water come from to make the rushing river that turns the turbines? Rain or snow. Without the sun there would be no rain or snow. All our weather is driven by the energy of the sun's heat. The sun warms different areas of the earth different amounts. That makes hot and cold areas of land and air. Air masses of different temperatures rise and fall. This air movement carries moisture high into the atmosphere where it is cooled and falls as rain or snow.

What about wind power? People have used windmills to do work for thousands of years, like grinding grain and pumping water. Windmills can also turn turbines to make electricity. Modern windmills that do this are placed in groups, usually on hills or near the sea where the wind blows steadily. Where does the wind get its energy? From the sun. That same movement of air that makes the rain and snow makes the wind.

We are all using the power of the sun to do work. But some ways of using it are making problems for the world. If we use the sun's energy in the form of fossil fuels - they are the fuels like petrol, coal and gas - pollution is caused when the fuels burn and produce waste products like sulphur.

Pollution damages the environment in several ways. It puts toxic gases into the air. It causes acid rain that kills trees. And remember, trees make the oxygen we need to breathe. Some of the gases given off when these fuels are burned are hanging high above the earth in a thick layer. This layer lets the sunshine in but doesn't let heat out. This means that the earth is slowly becoming warmer and warmer. That might sound nice but it will cause changes in our weather that will be disastrous. Lots of the water in the world is held as ice and snow in the coldest places, the North and South Poles. If that ice starts to melt, there will be much too much water in the oceans and some of the land will flood.

There is another problem with other kinds of pollution that is changing the way the sun shines on us. The sun is very, very powerful. We do not receive all of the sun's energy. Some of it is deflected by a layer in our atmosphere called the ozone layer. This ozone gas keeps harmful sun energy from getting down to the earth. Now, there are some holes developing in the ozone layer and some harmful energy is getting through. The holes are caused by pollution made by people.

We need the sun's heat and light to live, but we need just the right amount of them. There are billions of people on earth now and they all use the sun's energy. They all want things that will make their lives better and that means using lots of energy. And using lots of energy is causing pollution. What is going to happen? Are there ways of using the sun's energy without causing pollution? Think about drying your clothes. If you put them into the dryer, you use electricity that has come from a generator that probably burns coal. That is causing pollution. If you hang the clothes out in the sun or wind to dry, no fuel is burnt to do the work. Can you think of other ways of doing work that will not cause pollution?

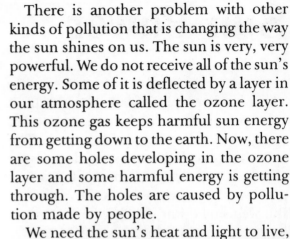

Save the Whales

You may have seen someone wearing a badge or seen a sticker in a car window that says 'Save the Whales'. Some people are very concerned for the safety of the whales because lots of them are being killed every year.

Whales are mammals, like human beings, dogs, cats, horses and many other animals. Mammals have some characteristics in common. They breathe air, give birth to live babies and feed them with milk. Whales live in the sea but they must surface to breathe and their babies are born underwater and can swim straight away. The baby whale's parents care for it like other mammal parents care for their young. People who have studied whales have come to the conclusion that they are very intelligent animals. Whales have very big brains divided into three parts, much like human brains. They even have a means of communicating with each other that is like a language of sounds. Some whales are enormous. Blue whales are the largest animals that have ever lived on the earth - larger than dinosaurs. Sperm whales have the biggest brains of any animal that has ever lived. Whales are the gentle, friendly giants of the deep.

Dolphins are some of the smallest whales. They need protecting, too. Each year thousands are killed. Some die by accident in tuna-fishing nets. Japanese fishermen slaughter them just because they eat the same kinds of fish the Japanese fishermen want to catch. Dolphins seem to like and trust people. They sometimes come quite close to swimmers as if they are curious and what to make friends.

Why do whales need saving? For centuries, people have hunted and killed whales. For a long time whales provided people with products they could get nowhere else. A whale's body contains lots of oil. Before electricity, this oil was burned in lamps for light. Later, it was used for making things such as margarine, soap and lipstick. Vitamins and medicines were obtained from parts of the animal. Also, some people ate the meat of whales. It was an important source of protein in the diets of some northern peoples. Today, however, no one needs to kill whales for these products. All the products that were made from a dead whale are now made from other things. For example, whale oil is no longer needed for light. Margarine, lipstick and soap are made from oils that can be extracted from various kinds of seeds. And people who live in countries where whale meat was eaten do not need it any more. They have plenty of beef, chicken, lamb and other animals to use for food. But some people want to eat whale because they like the taste and it is considered to be a real luxury. People in Japan, Norway and Iceland eat whale meat for enjoyment.

Who is saving the whales? There is an organisation called the International Whaling Commission. It is made up of people from nations that want to still allow whaling but want to control how many whales are killed. They are worried that if too many whales are killed, there will be none left. If that happens, they will not be able to make any more money from whaling. Other people believe no more whales should be killed at all. Greenpeace and the Worldwide Fund for Nature are two organisations that are trying to stop whaling altogether. Because people have shown their concern about whales, some countries have passed new laws that help look after them. In the United States, for example, tuna fishermen must use nets from which dolphins can escape if they get caught in them. Some fishing fleets even have divers on board their boats who go into the water and show the dolphins the way to escape. You may have seen a little blue symbol on a tin of tuna that tells you the tuna was caught in dolphin-friendly nets.

Why save the whales? Saving the whales means saving them from extinction. The balance of nature on our planet depends on all species living together in harmony. If one species dies out then the balance of nature is disturbed and life becomes difficult or impossible for other kinds of animals. If we are to keep the earth healthy, we must take care of all the plants and animals on it.

Seeking Refuge

It is impossible to know exactly how many refugees there are in the world today. The United Nations estimates there are 18 million refugees running from different dangers. Some are running from famine. You can see them on television and in the newspapers. They are walking skeletons, too weak to brush the flies from their faces. They die by the thousands in camps and on roads along which they wander in search of anything to eat. The famine is the result of drought but also of fighting in their countries.

Some are running from war. There are many long and cruel wars being fought around the world. You may have heard of some of them. Yugoslavia and Somalia appear most often in the news. But there are armed struggles going on in many other places: in Southeast Asia, southern Africa, Guatemala, Peru and many others.

In some countries there is not outright warfare but there are governments so repressive that they drive their own people out of the country in fear. There are so many things to run from and so few places to run to. What can the refugees do? Where can they go?

Some countries are prepared to take refugees and give them temporary safety. Some are prepared to let refugees enter and remain. But fewer and fewer countries are willing to do either. Many governments are making new laws that change the way they take refugees. Britain and Germany, for example, are reducing the numbers of refugees they will take. Some countries like Japan have never taken many. But there are still people fleeing from danger. They cross national borders and find safety from immediate danger in the next country. Such countries are called countries of first asylum - this means the country where the refugees first find refuge. But often that country also has problems of its own, and many refugees find themselves living in temporary camps in very poor countries. The Mozambican refugees, for example, usually found themselves in camps in Malawi. Malawi is a very poor country and could not afford to look after all the people who ran from the war in Mozambique. There were nearly two million of them and they had no food, housing or money to buy either. Many left home with only the clothes they were wearing. There is a heavy burden placed on the governments of countries of first asylum because they must look after all the extra, needy people who seek refuge there.

Once refugees have reached the safety of a camp in a country of first asylum, they hope to be relocated to a country where they can live in relative safety until the day when they can return home.

Many people think refugees want to leave home and never return. This is very rarely the case. Most refugees look forward to the day when they will return to their own homes again. They often find that they have to wait so long for the problems in their countries to be solved that they become accustomed to life in the new countries.

Refugees who do settle in another country often live in groups and keep their own customs alive. Many make positive contributions to their new countries. Albert Einstein the famous mathematician, for example, was a refugee. Vietnamese refugees who fled to the United States after the Vietnam war have worked very hard. Many of their children have done very well at school and university and have become doctors and lawyers.

Other groups of refugees have been in camps for so long that they have established communities in them. The Palestinians lost their homeland in the aftermath of the Second World War and the establishment of the new nation of Israel. Hundreds of thousands of Palestinians found themselves homeless in their own land. Bitter fighting broke out between the Palestinians and Israelis and as a result, the Palestinian people have been confined to refugee camps for over forty years. That means that there is a whole generation of Palestinians who have never had a country of their own. But they have kept their culture alive in the camps. They have established their own government, schools, universities and other services that make a country. They are a proud and patriotic people - but they are still refugees.

Because there have been problems in the past with large numbers of refugees seeking asylum in countries which do not want them, recently some refugees have not been allowed to cross national borders. Therefore they cannot escape from

the dangers in their own country. Busloads of Yugoslavian refugees have been stuck at border crossings, hoping to obtain travel documents that would allow them to cross. Some were sent back into danger because no country would promise to take them in.

Refugee camps where people wait, wasting their lives, sometimes for years are not the long term answer to the refugee problem. Sending people back into danger is not the answer. Many people think the answer lies in eliminating the danger from which refugees flee. Refugees would be happy to stay at home if they could. International organisations such as the United Nations are working toward bringing that about but they lack resources and political support to enforce peace.

Edward Jenner

Have you ever had an injection? If so, you were probably being immunised. That means you were being given an injection of weakened or dead bacteria or virus so your body would fight against it. In fighting the injected substance and winning, your body would build a defence against the real disease and you would not catch it. A number of dangerous and troublesome childhood illnesses have been fought in this way. Or maybe you have had a bad cut or puncture wound and then been given an injection against tetanus so you would not get that painful and life-threatening illness. How did the practice of injecting illness causing substances to fight illness get started?

Until two hundred years ago, mankind was plagued by an illness called smallpox. It killed many people who got it. People who survived might be left deaf or mentally subnormal. And they were terribly scarred. A small, deep pit was left on the skin wherever the victim had a pustule. Many people were covered with these pitted scars.

A young man called Edward Jenner was apprenticed to a country surgeon in Gloucestershire. He travelled round the countryside, helping to treat the ill and he became interested in smallpox. He had had it himself as a small boy and survived. He noticed two important things about the illness. People who had it and survived never got it again, and also milkmaids seldom got it. Milkmaids were women whose job it was to look after and milk cows. They did, however, get another, similar but much less severe illness called cowpox.

Some people had believed for some time that a person could be protected from smallpox by purposely infecting him with pus from the pox of someone with smallpox but attempts to do this often proved fatal.

Jenner decided to try to find a safer way to protect people from smallpox. He proceeded in a careful and scientific way. He believed that cowpox and smallpox were similar enough so that cowpox might protect milkmaids from smallpox. Milkmaids were renowned for their beauty. They seldom had scarred faces because they seldom had smallpox. They did, however, get cowpox. The pustules of cowpox that milkmaids got on their hands looked very much like smallpox in the early stages. Jenner knew that cowpox was a much less serious disease than smallpox and he thought if he could use fluid from cowpox pustules to immunise against smallpox, it would be much less dangerous. Jenner took many years and much hard, scientific work to devise a method of doing this.

Eventually he felt his methods were safe enough to test. An eight-year-old boy named James Phipps and a milkmaid named Sarah Nelmes were to help Edward Jenner make scientific history. Sarah Nelmes developed cowpox. Jenner took some of the cowpox pus from one of her pustules and inserted it into the arm of

James Phipps. Before long James became ill with cowpox, but then he recovered. Then Jenner had to inject the boy with smallpox matter to see if the cowpox had made him immune. Jenner must have been very certain he was right because if he was not, the boy would most probably die of smallpox.

So he injected him and the boy did not get the disease and Jenner knew he was right about preventing smallpox. Introducing diseased fluid into a well person

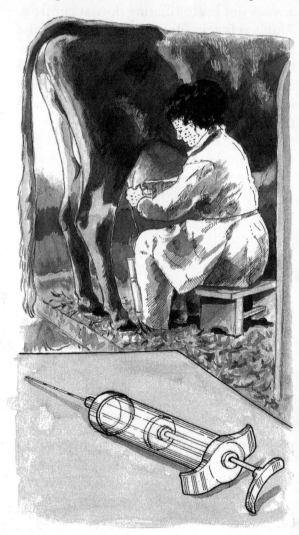

became known as vaccination and the fluid as vaccine. The words come from the Latin word *vacca*, meaning cow because of Jenner's use of cowpox.

Jenner's work continued and the importance of his discovery became known in many countries. More and more people wanted to be injected with cowpox so they would not get smallpox. The Emperor Napoleon of France had his army vaccinated because he knew how important it was to have soldiers well enough to fight. The President of the United States, Thomas Jefferson, introduced the idea of vaccination to the American people.

The story doesn't stop there. Vaccination against smallpox has been so successful that the disease has been completely eradicated. No one in the world gets it any more. The last recorded case of smallpox was in Somalia in 1977. Because there is still live smallpox in laboratories where scientific experimentation is carried out into the nature of disease, there is still vaccine available just in case smallpox should break out of the laboratory and threaten to spread again.

The Samurai Warriors

Samurai warriors were the knights of Japan. They were a special class of highly trained fighters who were greatly respected and feared. The tradition of the Samurai was strong in Japan from the 12th to the 19th century. For many hundreds of years before that, Japan had an Emperor but eventually he lost power and Japan broke up into small principalities, each ruled by a Daimyo. The Daimyos kept their own armies and these were the Samurai.

The Samurai were not only fighters. They were highly cultured and learned people. They were expected to write poetry and perform traditional dances. They were expected to be perfect in their daily lives and in their fighting skills. They had to obey their masters without question. Allegiance to the Daimyo came before friendship, family or self. Honour was all important to the Samurai. If they lost honour, their lives were worthless. Many committed suicide because they had lost their honour. This was done in the ritual called seppuku. To commit suicide this way, a warrior cut open his own stomach. Then a comrade would cut his head off with a very sharp sword. No Samurai would live without honour.

Samurai warriors could fight equally well on foot or on horseback. They used swords of various kinds and were also able to defend themselves well in hand to hand combat using the techniques of jujutsu.

Samurai wore special armour, helmets and masks that marked them as special warriors. They shaved a deep V in the hair on the tops of their heads, leaving the very top long, to be tied into a knot at the back. This, with their distinctive weapons and robes or armour were the insignia of a Samurai.

There were also women who were Samurai. They fought fiercely and well and followed the same code of honour as the men. Their allegiance was to their husbands or fathers who were Samurai rather than to the Daimyo. The children of Samurai were brought up in the same traditions as their fathers.

The Samurai must have been fearsome opponents to face in battle. They fought with a ferocity that can only come when the fighter knows he will fight to the death. When he killed an opponent, he cut the head off and took it back to the Daimyo. The more important the people whose heads he collected in battle, the greater his reward would be.

But as the world changed, there was less need for the private armies of Samurai. The Daimyo lost their power as Japan traded and communicated more and more with the outside world. Power was concentrated in the hands of traders and merchants instead of the Daimyo. One of the last important things the Samurai warriors did was to put an emperor back on the throne of Japan. Eventually they lost their special privileges and became ordinary Japanese citizens, but their deeds are still remembered in stores and poetry.

72

Ideas Man

Leonardo da Vinci leaned over his drawing board. His long beard and hair fell over his dark cloak. his left hand moved deftly, sketching. He drew a flying machine. It had a screw-shaped sail on the top, designed to rotate and lift the machine off the ground. It was, in fact, the first drawing of a helicopter. The most remarkable thing about this scene is that it took place in about 1520. The helicopter was not successfully invented and flown until the 1930s. So Leonard da Vinci had the idea 400 years too soon.

This was not the only idea Leonardo had. He was one of the greatest thinkers, inventors and artists of all time. He came up with lots of ideas for things we use today. He designed a bicycle and he even had the idea for ball-bearings in the wheels to reduce friction. He designed portable suspension bridges, mechanical diggers, exploding cannon balls, the distillation process and even a suit which would allow men to work and breathe underwater. But in Leonardo's time it was not possible to build most of the things he designed because knowledge of building materials had not progressed far enough. He had exciting ideas about forces and energy and about how the human body worked. He spent a great deal of time dissecting corpses to discover how our muscles make our bones move and why we look the way we do. This study of human anatomy helped him to become one of our greatest painters.

Leonardo was fascinated with birds. He observed them for long hours, watching how they used their wings and the air currents to fly. He used his observations and his considerable ability at mathematics to design flying machines. He loved birds and one story about him says that he would go to the marketplace, buy all the caged birds and set them free. It was his love of birds and other animals that would not allow him to kill and dissect them for his studies of anatomy. He even refused to eat animals, being a strict vegetarian.

But for all his love of animals, his peaceful nature and the loving eye with which he painted beautiful religious pictures, he still had to earn a living. When Leonardo was alive, Italy was divided into four separate states and the princes that ruled them fought among themselves. Because of this, there was always a need for new weapons of war. Leonardo offered his inventive mind to the service of one of the princes and designed many ingenious weapons and defences for him. He also designed war materials like ladders and bridges.

Leonardo kept notebooks of all his drawings for inventions and ideas about physics. He carefully annotated the drawings with mirror writing. Because he was left-handed, it was easier for him to write backwards. His wonderful paintings show how well he saw the world and how well he could paint what he saw. His notebooks show what an enquiring and inventive mind he had. He was one of the world's geniuses.

FABLES AND FOLK STORIES

The Clever Elf

Once upon a time there was a light-hearted little elf who lived in a splendid old forest. Everyone knows that elves keep pots of gold and this little elf had done very well for himself. He had a substantial pot of gold buried between the roots of one of the trees in the forest.

There also lived in the forest other creatures and amongst them was a greedy, sour old troll. He was big and hairy and as unpleasant as the elf was light-hearted.

One day the elf was skipping through the forest in his best red jerkin and green trousers, feeling very fine indeed. And as he skipped, he sang to himself: 'I've got a pot of gold under a tree! Nobody knows where it is but me!'

The horrid old troll had been sleeping fitfully in a pile of rotting leaves when he heard the elf coming along. The word "gold" immediately caught his ear and he listened to the elf's song. He saw his opportunity to take the elf's gold for himself. He crept behind a big beech tree beside the path and waited for the elf to come by.

The elf was so happy that it never occured to him to be careful. As he passed the tree the troll grabbed him by the scruff of his neck.

'Which tree?' bellowed the troll at the elf.

The elf turned away from the troll's hot, stinking breath.

'Take me to your pot of gold or I'll bite your head off!'

The elf took one look at the troll's teeth and decided he could indeed bite a head off.

'Alright. Put me down and I'll take you to my tree.'

There is one important thing you should know about elves: They cannot tell lies. They just can't.

So the elf led the troll through the forest to his particular tree beneath which his pot of gold was buried.

The troll, who was more than a little stupid, said, 'I haven't got my spade. You stay here by your tree while I go get it. And I'll tie this red handkerchief to a branch of the tree so you can't try to fool me.' With

that the troll took the elf's red handkerchief from his jerkin pocket and tied it to a branch of the tree.

'Promise you won't take this handkerchief off the tree!' he said threateningly to the elf.

'I promise,' said the elf. And elves never break promises.

So the troll went off to get his spade.

The elf was busy but he didn't break his promise.

When the troll came back, the red handkerchief was still on the tree but there were also red hankerchiefs on hundreds and hundreds of trees.

The elf laughed and laughed and skipped away as the troll started digging. He is probably still digging.

The Dinner of Smells

Nasrudin was one of the mullahs, or teachers, about whom Muslims tell many stories. He was clever and kind and had a good sense of humour.

One day a poor man was walking in a busy street when his nose picked up the wonderful smell of food cooking. The poor man followed his nose until he was standing outside the expensive restaurant from which the smells were escaping. He breathed deeply, drinking in the aromas. Because he was a poor man, he had to content himself with just smelling the food. He turned to walk away but the restaurant owner came running after him.

'Come back here! I saw you feasting on my smells. Now you must pay!'

The poor man was astonished but because he felt humble in the presence of the rich man he said, 'I am poor. I have no money. I cannot pay.'

'No money,' said the rich man. 'Then we will go to the judge. He will sort you out.'

The poor man knew the judge was a rich man like the restaurant owner. When they arrived at the court the two men greeted each other like friends and the poor man knew there was little chance he would be dealt with fairly.

The rich man told the judge what had happened and that he wanted the poor man to pay. The judge thought it was a very unusual case. He didn't know how to rule on the matter so he sent the two men away, telling them to return the next day to hear his decision.

The poor man was despondent. He was afraid he would be made to pay a lot of money and he had nothing. He spent a sleepless night and the next morning he went along to the court. On the way he met Nasrudin, the mullah. He knew Nasrudin was kind and fair and he told him the whole story.

Nasrudin thought for a moment and then smiled to himself. Yes, he would go along to the court and argue on the poor man's behalf.

They arrived before the judge. Immediately, he began to tell the poor man off in very insulting terms. He insisted the poor man must pay the restaurant owner for the

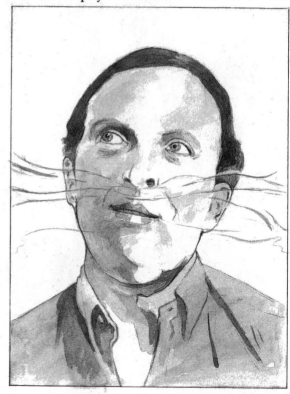

dinner of smells. He set the price very high.

Nasrudin interrupted the proceedings and said: 'I am this man's friend and I will pay for him.'

'Very well,' said the judge and the rich man together.

Nasrudin took a leather purse from inside his cloak. He held it to the rich man's ear and shook it. The coins inside jingled.

'Do you hear that?' he asked.

'Certainly I hear it,' replied the rich man.

'Well then, you are paid,' said Nasrudin. 'The poor man smelled your food and you heard his money. You are even.'

The judge and rich man had to give in to such a persuasive person as Nasrudin. The poor man paid nothing for the dinner of smells except the sound of money.

The Full Room

Once upon a time in India there was a very rich man. He was growing old and he had to decide which of his three sons would become head of the family when he died. He wanted to be sure that the son who would take over from him was clever so he devised a test for the three young men.

He called them together and gave them each one penny. He told them to go to the market and buy enough to fill the store room. He didn't say with what. It was up to them what they bought. He didn't know what to expect but he hoped at least one of his sons would be equal to the task. Their resourcefulness would determine which of them was clever enough to become head of the family.

At the end of the next day the first son came to his father and said he would like to try to fill the store room with the penny's worth of straw he had bought. His father agreed to put the straw to the test. The son beckoned the straw merchant and his helpers to come into the store room with their huge bundles of straw. They stacked it up but it did not fill the space. The first son tried breaking the bundles and fluffing the straw but it still did not fill the store room. He had failed.

The next day the second son returned home from market and asked his father if he could try filling the store room. He had bought a penny's worth of sand. Several porters filed into the store room and dumped their loads of sand but it came far from filling the space. And it was no good trying to fluff up the sand! The second son had failed.

The third son was gone the whole next day. He did not return until after dark. When he did return, he was carrying nothing but a very small parcel. He asked his father to let him go into the store room alone. He said when he had filled it, he would call his father to come and see.

The third son went inside the dark room and opened his parcel. He took out a candle and some matches. He stood the candle on the floor in the middle of the room and lit it. The room was filled with light!

He called his father and his brothers to come to the store room. They all had to agree that he had indeed filled the room for a penny. The third son was to become the head of the family.

The Tortoise and the Hare

The story of the tortoise and the hare is a very old one. In the version we usually hear, the fast hare challenges the slow tortoise to a race. The hare is so confident he will win that he doesn't try very hard. He stops frequently to rest and refresh himself. The tortoise meanwhile plods along, never stopping. In the end the tortoise crosses the finishing line first and wins the race. The moral is: Slow and steady wins the race.

There is a different version of this story that comes from Africa. It is told by the Swazi people and it gives the tortoise a little more credit for being clever.

Tortoise had been the target of lots of teasing on the part of Hare because he was so slow. Hare never missed an opportunity to make fun of him. One day, in jest, Hare challenged Tortoise to a race. He was sure Tortoise would decline and then Hare could tease him about that, too. To Hare's surprise, Tortoise accepted the challenge. But he asked specially that they make it a long race. Tortoise wanted to race ten kilometres to the lake. Tortoise also asked for several days to get into shape for the race. Hare agreed to both conditions.

Tortoise had to prepare for the race, but not in the way Hare expected. Secretly, Tortoise went round to his relatives and made a bargain with all his cousins who were about his size. He told each of them to place themselves along the route of the race. As hare approached, they were to pretend to be Tortoise and move as fast as they could in the direction of the lake. He, Tortoise, would go along to the lake and wait there for the big finish. Tortoise's cousins thought it was a wonderful plan because it gave them all a chance to get even with that tease, Hare.

The day of the big race came. Hare and a tortoise stood on the starting line. Hare hadn't the faintest idea that the tortoise standing there with him was not THE Tortoise. The starting gun went and hare took off like a shot. The tortoise plodded over the starting line. Hare tore along leaving a trail of dust. He was sure Tortoise was far, far behind. He rounded a bend and who did he see ahead of him? Tortoise! (Or so he thought, but we know it was really another of Tortoise's cousins.) He couldn't

believe it. He put on more speed and left Tortoise in the dust again.

On he ran, confident that Tortoise was never going to catch up. Up a steep hill he went and over the brow of the hill who should he see up ahead? Tortoise! Hare couldn't believe it. Now if Hare had been as clever as he was fast, he might have guessed something was not quite right about this whole thing. But he wasn't clever and he thought Tortoise was somehow passing him. He kept running faster and he kept finding tortoise in front of him. Finally, as he neared the lake, his legs gave way beneath him and he collapsed, exhausted. He heard footsteps. He opened his eyes and who should be coming over to him with a drink of water from the lake? You've guessed it — Tortoise. And I am afraid Tortoise took full advantage of the situation and had his turn at teasing Hare.

Baba Yaga

Folk tales and fables were often used to warn children to behave themselves or they would suffer dire consequences. In them, children are told they will meet with a terrible fate at the hands of villains like monsters or witches if they don't do as they are told.

Russian children were told stores of the witch Baba Yaga. It was said she rode through the sky in a mortar, using the pestle as a rudder. She lived in the forest in a house that walked around on hen's feet. She ate children.

This story is about a child who just missed being eaten.

A mother and father had to go to town and they left their little daughter Elena in charge of herself and her baby brother. She was told not to leave him alone for a moment because Baba Yaga's black geese were flying. They were out scouring the countryside for a child for Baba Yaga's dinner.

Elena promised to watch carefully after her brother and she meant to do just that. They played on the grass for it was a lovely day. Elena's friends came to see her and she began to play with them. Forgetting all about her baby brother, Elena wandered off with her friends, chatting and laughing. They left the baby unguarded. He gurgled and giggled to himself. The soft green grass tickled his tiny feet. He had no warning of the danger that approached from the sky.

Baba Yaga's black geese swooped down, grabbed him and flew off to the witch with a tasty baby for her dinner.

When Elena came back and found her brother gone she knew at once what had happened. In anxiety, and without a single thought for her own safety, she set off to the forest to find him.

On her way, Elena ran past a pond. She heard a small voice and, looking down she saw a fish that had become marooned on the shore.

'Elena!' cried the fish. 'Help me! Please put me back into the pond.'

Elena carefully lifted the fish back into the water.

'You have helped me and I will help you,' said the fish. He gave Elena a shell from the pond and said, 'Take this shell and, if you ever need help, throw it over your shoulder.'

Elena took the shell and ran on. Soon she came to a copse. As she ran between the trees she heard a small voice.

'Elena! Help me!'

Elena looked around and saw a squirrel with his foot caught in a trap. She carefully opened the trap and let the squirrel out.

'You have helped me and I will help you,' said the squirrel. He handed Elena a nut. 'Take this nut and, if you ever need help, throw it over your shoulder.'

Elena took the nut and ran on. Soon she came to a stream and as she climbed the stony bank she heard a small voice.

'Elena! Help me!'

Elena looked down and saw a mouse whose tail was caught under a large stone. She lifted the stone and let the mouse go free.

'You have helped me and I will help you,' said the mouse. He handed Elena a stone. 'Take this stone and, if you ever need help, throw it over your shoulder.'

Elena took the stone and ran on. She went into the thick forest. It was dark and damp and very frightening. Soon she came to the clearing where Baba Yaga's house stood on hen's feet. The door was open and Elena could see inside. Baba Yaga was asleep and snoring in great, loud, disgusting snorts. Elena's little brother was sitting on the floor by the witch's bed. Elena crept carefully up to the house and through the door. She grabbed her little brother and turned to run. But the black geese saw Elena stealing Baba Yaga's dinner and they honked and cackled until the witch woke up.

Elena ran as fast as she could, carrying her brother under her arm. Baba Yaga ran faster. Elena took the fish's shell from her pocket and threw it over her shoulder. With a great squelching noise a huge lake appeared between her and Baba Yaga. But Baba Yaga leaned down and drank the whole lake and kept on running.

Elena ran as fast as she could and took the squirrel's nut from her pocket and threw it over her shoulder. With a great splintering noise a wood grew between her and Baba Yaga. But Baba Yaga ate a wide path through the wood and kept on running.

Elena ran as fast as she could and took the mouse's stone from her pocket and threw it over her shoulder. With a great booming sound a huge mountain rose between her and Baba Yaga. Baba Yaga could not drink it or eat it or climb over it. She stopped running and went back home to the forest very angry indeed.

When Elena's mother and father came home from the town, Elena and her brother were playing peacefully on the grass. As a reward for having been so good, their parents brought them buns with currants and sugar.

Hippo Takes to the Water

The Kikuyu people of Africa believe in one great creator god they call N'gai. He made the world and all the plants and animals. This story is about the hippopotamus and how he came to live in the water.

When N'gai first made the hippo he sent him to live in the forests and on the vast grasslands of Africa. Hippo, having a huge mouth and an appetite as big, ate and ate. There was plenty for him to graze on and he grew very fat indeed. He was quite contented until he realised he was beginning to have some difficulty getting around. Even the shortest walk was very difficult and it made him sweat and puff. The heat of the noon day sun made him increasingly uncomfortable. The daily walk to the river to drink became more and more unpleasant for him.

One day as he stood up to his fat ankles in the river, drinking his fill, he noticed how contented the little fishes looked as they floated effortlessly in the water. They looked like they weighed nothing at all as they drifted peacefully in the currents.

'If only I could float about like the little fishes,' thought Hippo. 'It would certainly take the weight off my feet. It think I will ask N'gai to let me live in the river like the fishes.'

So Hippo called out to N'gai, 'N'gai, you are our good lord. Please have pity on me. The sun burns my tender skin and I am too fat to wander around grazing and walking to the river for a drink every day. Please let me live in the river with the little fishes.'

'No,' said N'gai. 'I cannot let you live with my little fishes for I love them as I love all my creatures and your appetite is so big I am sure you will eat my little fishes. You must continue to live on land.'

Hippo went back to grazing and was increasinly miserable. His tender skin burnt in the hot sun. The walk to the river seemed to get longer and longer. Hippo wept to see the little fishes so contented. He decided to go back to N'gai with a promise.

'N'gai!' called Hippo. 'What if I promise not to eat your fishes? Then will you let me live in the river?'

N'gai felt sorry for Hippo for he loved him as he loved all his creatures and he said, 'How can I be sure that you will not eat them? I will need some kind of proof.'

'But I promise,' said Hippo in a pitiful wail. 'Yes,' said N'gai, 'I know you promise but how will I know you have eaten only the plants that grow in the water and not the fishes? How will you show me that you have not broken your promise?'

Hippo thought long and hard and answered carefully. 'Great N'gai, each day, after I have eaten, I will come out of the water onto the river bank and I will scatter my dung with my tail so that you can see there are no fish bones in it.'

N'gai agreed and from that day to this, Hippo has lived happily in the river, eating only water plants. And he always scatters his dung with his tail.

Korean Folk Story

Once there was a man who had lived such a good life that, when he died, he went to Heaven. Just before entering he asked if he could be given a tour of Hell. Perhaps he wanted to see the misery which he had been spared by living such a good life. His wish was granted.

When he arrived he had a great surprise. There, in front of him, he saw a table covered with food. The table stretched as far as the eye could see and on it was a huge variety of foods. Just imagine your favourite foods: they were there. Just imagine the expensive foods you have probably only heard of: they were there. The man closed his eyes, thinking he had been imagining everything. But when he opened them again he realised that the magnificient food was in fact real. Was this really the Hell he'd heard such a lot about? Was there really such wonderful food in a place he had always feared being sent to? Surely not.

Then he notied something else. Everybody appeared absolutely miserable. There was not a smiling face to be seen. Moreover, all the people looked as if they were starving. How could that be so in a place where food was so abundant? His guide explained why. Everyone who entered Hell was given a pair of chopsticks two metres long and they had to eat their food holding them at the end. Can you imagine how difficult that would be? Can you imagine the contortions into which people forced their bodies to try and get just one taste of the succulent food? Despite all their efforts they were unsuccessful. What could be a worse punishment than being surrounded by such appetising food and being unable to eat it?

The Korean asked to be taken to Heaven. There he was once again surprised to see a table groaning with food. This one, too, stretched as far as the eye could see. The food was also as varied and as delicious as you could ever imagine. The people however looked much happier and were obviously well fed.

'I see,' said the Korean, 'in Heaven they don't have to eat with long chopsticks.' 'Oh yes they do,' explained the guide. 'Their chopsticks are exactly the same length as those you saw in Hell. They also have to be held at the end when the people are eating.'

'Well, how do you explain everyone looking so healthy and well fed?'

'That's easy,' replied the guide. 'They have discovered that if one person picks up the food and offers it to a friend then that friend will do the same for them. In that way, by helping each other, everyone gets fed.'

Getting Fire from Bandicoot

The Aborigine people of Australia tell many stories about their ancestors and the animals of their country. This one tells of a time long ago called the Nyitting time, when people did not yet have fire. It is the story of how the sparrowhawk and the pigeon got fire from the bandicoot who was trying to keep it for himself.

In the Nyitting time men and women ate their food raw and they could not get warm unless the sun shone. They wanted fire but they could not get it. The one who did have fire was Bandicoot and he was mean and greedy about it. He wanted it all to himself. Whenever he went out hunting, he took the fire with him, hidden under his tail.

People would call to Bandicoot, 'Share your fire with us!'

But Bandicoot was a liar as well and he would say, 'What fire? I haven't any fire.'

But the people could see the fire shining beneath Bandicoot's tail.

Sparrowhawk and his cousin Pigeon decided to help the people by getting fire from Bandicoot. They decided to go to Bandicoot and ask him for just a little of his fire.

Bandicoot saw them coming and hid the fire under his tail. But Sparrowhawk and Pigeon knew he had fire because he had been cooking meat and they could smell the delicious aroma.

'Give us just a little of your fire, Bandicoot,' they said.

Bandicoot was licking delicious, melted fat from his paws. 'I have no fire,' he said.

Sparrowhawk and Pigeon pretended to leave. They walked a little way off and whispered to each other, 'We will have to steal fire from Bandicoot. He is too greedy to give it away.'

Sparrowhawk and Pigeon watched Bandicoot for several days and one day they saw him with fire on his back. They crept out of hiding and surprised Bandicoot. They sat firmly on either side of him, pressing into him. They didn't say a word. They just pushed him this way and that and they moved him from his home

towards the sea. It was a long way but they travelled together, Sparrowhawk and Pigeon pushing Bandicoot.

Finally, they came to the sea. Then Bandicoot had a cunning idea. He tried to throw fire into the sea so it would go out and the people would not get it. Sparrowhawk and Pigeon were so angry at him that they threw Bandicoot into the sea but as they did, a spark flew off his fire and landed in Pigeon's beard and began to burn.

Pigeon and Sparrowhawk hurried away from the sea and put fire in every tree they found. Some burned fast and made ash and some burned slowly and made charcoal. The ash people could use for healing wounds and the charcoal people could use for fuel. And people cooked their meat and warmed their dwellings and were never cold again. All thanks to Sparrowhawk and Pigeon.

Daedalus and Icarus

There are many stories about the gods and heroes of ancient Greece. The Greeks believed their gods inhabited Mount Olympus and that they often came down from the mountain and manipulated the lives of ordinary people. They believed the gods squabbled amongst themselves and caused great calamity with their wilful ways. The Greeks also invented heroes and creatures that were part man and part beast. A number of exciting stories were born out of these combinations of truth and fiction. The story of Daedalus and Icarus is one of them.

During a time when Athens was at war with Crete, there lived a man named Daedalus. He was very clever and inventive. One of the things he made was a huge maze called the Labyrinth. He built it for King Minos of Crete as a prison for a creature called the Minotaur. The Minotaur had the head and shoulders of a bull and the lower body of a man. It was strong and cruel and King Minos sacrificed people to it. King Minos was going to sacrifice some prisoners of war to the Minotaur. His daughter, Ariadne, had fallen in love with one of the prisoners, Theseus, and she persuaded Daedalus to show them how to escape from the Labyrinth. Daedalus showed Theseus how to tie a string to the door of the Labyrinth and unwind it behind himself so he could follow this string and find his way out of the maze. Theseus killed the Minotaur and escaped.

King Minos was furious and he knew that Theseus must have had the help of Daedalus for no one else knew the secret of the Labyrinth. As a punishment, King Minos imprisoned Daedalus and his son Icarus in the Labyrinth. The high walls of the maze might have been a prison to most men but Daedalus was clever and he thought up a plan for escape.

Daedalus had watched the birds soaring overhead and he got an idea from them. Using feathers they had collected along with sticks and wax, Daedalus constructed a pair of wings for himself and a pair for Icarus. They strapped them to their arms and before they took flight, Daedalus cautioned his son.

'Icarus,' he said, 'Do not fly too low, for the spray from the sea will soak into the feathers and make them heavy and you will fall and drown. But do not fly too high for if you do, the sun will melt the wax in your wings and you will fall and drown.'

Icarus heard his father's warning, but he did not heed it. The two men escaped the maze, rising above it by flapping their wings. When they were flying like birds out over the ocean, Icarus's excitement overtook his good sense. He flew higher and higher, enjoying the feelings of power and freedom. He flew too high. And just as his father warned, the sun melted the wax in his wings. They fell apart and Icarus plummeted into the sea and drowned.

Daedalus flew on to safety, but alone, without the son who had not listened to his advice.

The Baker and the Fairies

Once upon a time in a village near Aberdeen in Scotland, there lived a woman who was an extraordinarily good baker. She was known for miles around and everyone wanted to buy her cakes and buns. In those days, Scotland hummed with fairies and their mischief and they, too, had heard about the wonderful cakes. Like everyone else, they were determined to have some.

One day when the baker was going home through the forest, the fairies dusted her with magic and she fell into a deep sleep by the side of the road. When she awoke, she found herself in the court of the king of the fairies.

'We have captured you,' he said, 'and you will live here with us and bake us endless cakes and buns.'

The baker might have been afraid and worried about being amongst the mischievous fairies but she didn't show it. She took her apron out of her basket and tied it round herself. 'Very well,' she said, 'I hope you have all the things I will need to make the cake.'

'Tell us what you need,' said the fairy king, 'and we will get it for you.'

'I think,' she said, teasing them a bit, 'we will start with a big, dark rich cake with currants and nuts!'

A shout of appreciation went up from the assembled numbers.

'Please hurry back to my house and bring me my biggest mixing bowl!'

A committee of fairies organised themselves and rushed off. In a flash they were back, a bit breathless from flying with the weight of the great mixing bowl.

'Now,' said the baker, 'I must have some of your finest flour.'

'We have none,' said the fairy king.

'Well, then, you will have to go along to my house and get some of my flour.'

'Go for the flour!' commanded the king. The flour was brought.

'Now we will need some fat!' announced the baker.

'We have not got fat either,' admitted the king. 'Send for the fat.'

Then she needed sugar, eggs, currants, nuts and spices. And of course, the fairies had none of them. So each time the baker asked for an ingredient, a committee of fairies had to fly off to her house and get what she needed.

Finally the ingredients were assembled.

'Now,' said the baker, 'all I need to do is mix it up!' And she started to measure the flour into the bowl. She stopped suddenly and said, 'I am so used to having my dear pussy cat rubbing round my ankles when I work. I do not think I can do this without him.'

'Send for the cat!' shouted the king.

The cat was brought and the baker continued to work. Suddenly she stopped again. 'Something is missing.'

'What is it now?' roared the fairy king.

'I am so used to having my dear little baby cooing contentedly in his cot that I cannot work without him,' said the baker.

'Send for the baby,' said the fairy king, holding his head.

The baby and the cot and all the things a baby needs were brought and the woman set to work again. She measured and mixed and measured and mixed. Then she stopped mixing and said, 'Something is wrong. I am so used to having my dear husband whittling a stick and whistling a tune while I work that I don't think I can carry on without him.'

'Send for the husband,' said the king in a most discouraged voice.

The husband was brought along.

Finally, the batter was mixed. It was thick and rich and smelled very promising.

'Now,' said the baker, smiling to herself, 'I will need my biggest pan.' Then turning pointedly to the king she added, 'Unless, of course, you have a big pan I can use . . .'

'No!' shouted the fairy king. He was becoming exasperated. 'Send for the pan!' The pan was sent for and the batter was spooned into it.

'Now,' said the baker, 'where is the oven?'

The fairy king could not believe his ears. 'We have no oven,' he said with resignation.

'Well,' said the baker, 'you will have to send some fairies to being me my oven — unless of course, you will let me take the cake home to bake it?'

'Yes', said the king, ready to give up the idea of the cake, 'by all means take the cake home and bake it.' He heaved a sigh and held his head in his hands.

'I have made this cake for the fairies,' said the baker, 'and the fairies shall have it. When it is baked I will leave it beside the road in the forest where I fell asleep. Not only that, but I will bake you a cake every week and leave it in that same place.'

The fairy king was delighted and being a proud king he promised that for every cake left there the baker would find ample payment. So the fairies let the woman and her husband and her baby and her cat go home to bake the cake.

Both the baker and the fairy king were as good as their words. Every week the baker left a cake where she said she would and she always found a tiny purse of fairy gold in payment.

Blue Willow

There is nothing as nice to eat off as a plate with blue decorations. Perhaps this is because there is no blue food and the blue colour gives some contrast. One of the nicest blue patterns is one of the most well known. It is the Blue Willow pattern. Many potteries make china with the Blue Willow pattern and though they may vary a little, basically the picture on all the plates is the same. It is a rather peaceful scene showing a pagoda, or Chinese building, by a lake. There is an ornate fence and there are several different kinds of trees. A boat with two people floats on the lake and overhead, two birds swoop in flight.

Some people think the plate tells a story. You can decide for yourself which came first, the plate or the story.

Once upon a time in old China there lived a miser named T'so Ling. He was very wealthy but very greedy. He liked having lots of gold and a beautiful house full of extravagant things. He was determined to keep all his riches for himself. The one truly lovely thing he had was a beautiful daugher named Koong-se. She was as sweet and kind as her father was mean and miserly. Old T'so Ling was determined that no one would marry his daughter — unless, of course, he was a very rich man, too.

T'so Ling didn't now Koong-se already loved a young man named Chang. Chang worked for T'so Ling. He was not rich because the miser was very stingy with the wages. Chang was a very hard worker and was kind and intelligent and he would have been a good husband for Koong-se. But T'so Ling was furious when he found out Chang and Koong-se were in love and wanted to get married. He insisted Koong-se would only marry a man as rich as himself. T'so Ling banished Chang and built a fence around all his lands.

T'so Ling then imprisoned Koong-se in a pagoda by the lake. She was guarded night and day so she could not run away and find Chang. T'so Ling told her she would have to marry his old friend Ta-chin who was also very rich. Koong-se wept and pleaded but her father would not listen. She would have to marry Ta-chin in the spring and that was that.

Koong-se sat in her pagoda and watched winter turn to early spring. She watched the different trees come into bud. She saw the catkins grow on the weeping willow and sadly she saw the peach tree was about to bloom. Soon it would be time for her to marry rich, old Ta-chin. But she never stopped hoping Chang would return and rescue her.

One day when the peach blossoms were almost out, Koong-se saw a tiny, toy boat floating on the lake. She picked it from the waters and found it contained a message from Chang telling her to be brave and be ready to escape with him.

The next day, as the peach blossoms opened, Ta-chin arrived with all his entourage. While everyone was watching him prancing about all puffed up and looking silly in too many fine clothes, Chang crept over the fence. He hid amongst the trees until it was dark and then he went to

Koong-se in the pagoda. He whispered to her and without a sound the two escaped into the night.

They ran through the garden and over the bridge, heading for a small boat Chang had waiting. But one of the guards saw them and soon T'so Ling, Ta-chin and the guard were chasing them over the bridge. Just in time Koong-se and Chang reached the boat and were able to sail away to the island where they lived happily — but not forever after, sad to say.

T'so Ling and Ta-chin kept searching for Koong-se and Chang. They were determined to punish both of them. The hunt went on for years while Koong-se and Chang lived a quiet, happy life on the tiny island. Old T'so Ling died but Ta-chin continued the search. One day his soldiers found the house on the island where Koong-se and Chang were living. Ta-chin's soldiers found Chang working in the orchard and killed him. Koong-se saw this and she was overcome with grief. She ran into their cottage and set it on fire. As the fire died down, out of the ashes flew two white doves. Koong-se and Chang had changed into doves and they flew away — this time to live happily ever after.

A Brave Lass

Once upon a time in Scotland thre lived a girl who was not afraid of anything. Her mother and father were both dead and she lived alone in a clearing in the forest. She had a small farm with a cow for milk and cheese, chickens for eggs, bees for honey, an apple tree and a tidy little garden for vegetables. What she could not grow or make for herself, she could get from the village shop by trading extra eggs or cheese or apples for them. The people in the village were very worried about her safety, living up there in the forest all by herself. Often they tried to persuade her to live in the village. They warned her about bears and wolves that might live in the forest, and spoke in hushed tones of fairies and goblins and ghosts. But she said she wasn't afraid of anything.

One evening as the sun went down behind the tall trees of the forest, the fearless lass went to the oatmeal bin to scoop herself some porridge oats for making supper. To her annoyance, she found the bin nearly empty. After she had made herself some supper, there would be no oatmeal left and then what would she have for breakfast? If she was to have porridge in the morning, she would have to get some oats ground that night. So she took up her sack of oats and set out to walk to the miller's to have him grind them.

It was no short walk to the miller's and the dark night closed in around her. She took no torch for she knew the way well.

She liked the cool darkness and the shuffle and crunch of her feet as she strode along the forest path. The noises of night birds and bats were as pleasant to her as the sounds of her farm animals. The dark branches of the trees that reached over the path made her feel safe. She was not afraid of anything.

When she reached the miller's it was very late indeed and the mill was locked up tight. But there was a light in the miller's house and so she knocked at the door.

'I'm sorry to call so late,' she said, 'but I have no porridge for the morning and I must ask you to please grind these oats for me.'

'No!' replied the miller. 'I never grind at night. You can wait until the morning or go home and come back again but I'll not go into the mill after dark.'

'Why ever not?' asked the fearless lass.

'Because,' said the miller lowering his voice in fear, 'there is a terrible goblin that lives under the floor of the mill. He never comes out in the daylight but if anyone grinds at night, he rises out of the floor. He beats them with his terrible club and frightens them nearly to death!'

The fearless lass could see from the way the miller's face had gone white as he spoke that he was truly afraid.

'Then give me the key to the mill and I will grind my own oats. I'm not afraid of any old goblin.'

So the fearless lass took the key and went across to the mill without giving the goblin a second thought. She let herself in. Moonlight streamed through the window and in its white light the fearless lass could see her way around. She poured her oats onto the stone and began to grind them. The rhythm of the sone vibrated the floor and the rafters creaked and groaned. Mice and beetles scurried into their holes.

Suddenly, above the sounds of the grinding wheel, there rose a terrible howl. The fearless lass just kept grinding. It grew louder and louder. Then when there was no more room for any more noise, up from beneath the floor rose a most terrible goblin. He swung a huge spiked club around his head. His green hair dripped slime and his mouthful of pointed teeth dribbled boiling spittle. His popping eyes rolled in his filthy face.

'Who dares grind at night?!' he roared.

'I do,' said the brave lass fearlessly. 'And don't bother me. I need my porridge for the morning.'

The goblin flew at her, flailing about with his club. The fearless lass stuck out her foot and tripped him up. She grabbed the club from his hairy hand and gave him some terrible clouts about the head and shoulders. Then she picked him up by the scruff of his neck and thrust him between the millstones. She set the mill grinding again. The goblin cried out for help and the miller, safe in his house, was sure it was the lass who was crying out. Of course, it is impossible to kill a goblin but when he was well and truly ground and scraped and bruised, the fearless lass stopped the wheel.

'And now, you hideous thing, can the miller grind at night?' asked the lass. 'Or shall I grind you a little longer?'

'Grind night and day but grind me no more,' wailed the goblin. And the fearless lass let him go. He slid under the floor and because of the fright he had received he left the mill and was never seen again.

Otter's Babies

One day the mother otter said to the deer, 'Will you please look after my babies? I must go to catch some crayfish in the river.'

The deer agreed. But when the otter returned home with her catch she found her babies had all been crushed to death!

'Who killed my babies?' cried the otter to the deer.

'I am very sorry,' said the deer, 'but as you well know I am the chief of the war dance. The heron came and sounded the war gong with his long beak, so I had to dance the war dance. I forgot your babies were there and danced on them and crushed them.'

'This is terrible,' said the otter. 'The one responsible for the deaths of my babies must be punished. We will go to the King.'

So the otter and the deer went to the King. And the King said to the deer, 'Did you kill the otter's babies?'

'Yes, your Majesty,' said the deer, 'but I didn't mean to. As you know I am the chief of the war dance and when the heron sounded the war gong, I had to dance. I forgot the otter's babies were there and danced on them and crushed them.'

'Send for the heron!' said the King. When the heron came the King said to him, 'Were you the one who sounded the war gong?'

'Yes, your Majesty,' said the heron, 'but I had to. As you know I am the chief gonger of the war gong and I had to sound it because I saw the lizard wearing his sword.'

'Send for the lizard!' said the King. When the lizard came the King said, 'Were you wearing your sword?'

'Yes, your Majesty,' said the lizard, 'but I had to. As you know I am the keeper of the sword. I wore it because the tortoise came wearing his armour.'

'Send for the tortoise!' said the King. When the tortoise came the King said, 'Were you wearing your armour?'

'Yes, your Majesty,' said the tortoise, 'but I had to. I saw the frog carrying his great long pike.'

'Send for the frog!' said the King. When the frog came the King said, 'Were you carrying your great long pike?'

'Yes, your Majesty', said the frog, 'but I had to. I saw the crayfish had shouldered his lance.'

'Send for the crayfish!' said the King. When the crayfish came the King said, 'Had you shouldered your lance?'

'Yes, your Majesty,' said the crayfish, 'but I had to. I saw the otter coming down to the river to kill my children.'

'Hmmm,' said the King, thinking it through. 'In that case, the otter is responsible for killing her own children and the deer cannot be blamed.'

However, the King did not punish the otter, for he was a wise King and he saw that the death of her babies was punishment enough.

POEMS

Fireworks

By James Reeves

They rise like sudden fiery flowers
   That burst upon the night,
Then fall to earth in burning showers
   Of crimson, blue and white.

Like buds too wonderful to name,
   Each miracle unfolds,
And catherine-wheels begin to flame
   Like whirling marigolds.

Rockets and Roman candles make
   An orchard of the sky,
Whence magic trees their petals shake
   Upon each gazing eye.

London Trees

By Margaret Stanley Wrench

Long before the houses came
The London trees were here,
The sycamore with leaves like hands,
The poplar like a spear

The pear tree heaped with warm, white
snow,
The plane tree's piebald bark,
The elm with crinkled, pleated leaves,
The fir tree, plumed and dark.

And though the houses change and fall
And tall flats life like towers,
Year after year the trees still give
Us shadows, leaves and flowers.

95

Television Aerials

by Stanley Cook

Television aerials
Look like witches' brooms.
When they finish flying
They leave them on the roof.

Television aerials
Are sticks to prod the sky
To make clouds full of rain
Hurry by.

Television aerials
Reach above chimney tops
To make a perch
Where tired birds can stop.

Television aerials
Are fixed to the chimney side
To rake us songs and pictures
Out of the sky.

The Mole

By Bob Loosemore

There was a stretch
of marshy meadow bank,
by which I dreamed;
where king-cups reigned,
wild garlic stank,
and 'peckers tapped, unseen
their hollow news
. . . to me alone.

I knew so many
hiding places where
tall, fearless daffodils
could nod,
silent in approval
sure, in the rich Devon sod,
of being left in peace,
disturbed by none,
. . . but me alone.

Come, see the restless Mole
that nibbles slowly
at our brown soil;
now lazy in deep pools,
now chattering and chuckling
over semi-precious stones,
fashioned in constant turmoil
. . . for me alone.

Winter

From *Love's Labours Lost*
by William Shakespeare

When icicles hang by the wall,
    And Dick the shepherd blows his nail,
And Tom bears logs into the hall,
    And milk comes frozen home in pail,
When blood is nipped, and ways be
    foul,
Then nightly sings the staring owl,
        Tu-whit, tu-who!
        A merry note,
When greasy Joan doth keel the pot.

When all around the wind doth blow,
    And coughing drowns the parson's saw,
The birds sit brooding in the snow,
    And Marian's nose looks red and raw,
When roasted crabs hiss in the bowl,
Then nightly sings the staring owl,
        Tu-whit, tu-who!
        A merry note,
When greasy Joan doth keel the pot.

Cloud In The Wind

by Bob Loosemore

Goes where the wind blows,
Fighting no will;
Reaps as the sun sows,
Cloud in the wind.

No chartered course takes.
When once has passed,
No passage back makes;
Cloud in the wind.

Born every morning,
No two alike;
Mixing and merging,
Cloud in the wind.

Clearly defined when
Seen from afar;
From close confusing,
Cloud in the wind.

Love will appear thus,
Blown from the sea;
Happy and free, like a
Cloud in the wind.

The Wind of Change

By Rod McKuen

Quietly, like the breeze that blows the
   olive tree
The wind of change has come down
   from the hills
To bring me home again
Through the last mile of sunshine.

As easily as the moon makes patterns on
   the lifeless lake,
Man grinds the flowers of the fields
   beneath his heels,
And you wonder if he feels love,
   or even boredom,
And my friends the wind of change is
   asking questions.

Suddenly, there are now so many
   changes everywhere,
So many men who think even God
   looks small
When they are walking tall;
And the wind of change is smiling.

Could it be that his smile is just another
   kind of frown,
Because he knows the world is finally
   falling down
And going back to dust and if we trust
   the men who trample on the ground
Emptiness is all that we can ever hope
   to ask for.

Listen to hear the sound of the dying
   grass bleed.
It is bleeding for man, and the fool he
   just won't understand.
Is it too late to change
The wind of change?

Cats

By Rod McKuen

Cats have the best of it
I suppose they always have.
Curled up in Autumn
back behind the stove,
swaggering through shrubbery
in the summer months.
Pirates seeking treasure
be it hapless mouse or moth.

When ready,
for some human contact,
usually at mealtime
or when you're busy
    doing something
they know they can disturb,
they're smarter than possums
but they do not extend
    lapdog submission.
A cuddle or a belly rub
perhaps a scratch behind the ear
    is quite enough.

Cats, I reckon, have it all —
admiration and an endless sleep
and company only when they want it.

Song of the Sky Loom

An American Indian Chant

O our Mother the Earth, O our Father
    the Sky,
Your children are we, and with tired backs
We bring you the gifts that you love.
Then weave for us a garment of
    brightness;
May the warp be the white light of morning,
May the weft be the red light of evening,
May the fringes be the falling rain,
May the border be the standing rainbow.
Thus weave for us a garment of brightness
That we may walk fittingly where
    birds sing,
That we may walk fittingly where
    grass is green
O our Mother the Earth, Our our Father
    the Sky!

Vagabonds

By Langston Hughes

We are the desperate
Who do not care,
The hungry
Who have nowhere
To eat,
No place to sleep,
The fearless
Who cannot
weep.

STORIES FROM SACRED BOOKS

When Jesus was Twelve

After the story of his birth there is only one mention in the Bible of the childhood of Jesus. This tells the story of his visit to Jerusalem at the age of twelve. It was the first time he was allowed to accompany his parents to Jerusalem to celebrate the Feast of the Passover. This feast was held every year in memory of the time when God had helped the Israelites to escape from their slavery in Egypt. It was still the most important festival in the Jewish calendar.

The days before Jesus' journey must have been very exciting. Many pre-parations had to be made for the three day journey. A number of families from Nazareth travelled together and Jesus would have had great fun playing with the other children.

When they reached Jerusalem the excitement increased. The streets were thronged with people. Jews had travelled from many countries around as well as from all over Israel. Joseph and Mary showed Jesus all the sights of the great city, but as far as he was concerned, it was the Temple which was of most interest. He walked through the outer courtyard where the money changers changed the foreigner's money so they could buy animals to sacrifice. He also listened to the priests and the learned men talking about the history of the Jews and explaining the scriptures. He probably stood in the doorway of the Inner

Temple as he was too young to enter. From there he could watch Joseph sacrifice the Paschal lamb.

After three days the people from Nazareth gathered together for their return journey. Mary and Joseph, thinking that Jesus was travelling with the parents of a friend, left Jerusalem without him. It was only at night-time, when they came to set up camp, that they discovered that he was missing. They returned immediately to Jerusalem.

After many hours of searching they found Jesus sitting amongst the learned men in the Temple. Everyone was amazed at his words and wisdom. He asked some very difficult questions. The learned men were surprised that Jesus could answer all their questions, too.

Mary was angry. 'My son, why have you done this to us? Think how your father and I have looked for you in great distress.'

Jesus stood up and said, 'Why did you seek me? Do you not know that I must be in my Father's House?'

Mary did not understand what Jesus meant but this incident shows us that by the age of twelve Jesus knew exactly who he was and what he had to do.

The incident also shows us that he knew the Jewish scriptures well and was clever at answering questions. Later in his life this was to be a very important ability. As he became more and more popular with the people of Israel, the Priests and Pharisees became jealous of him. They tried to catch him out on many occasions.

One day Jesus and his disciples were walking through some cornfields on the Sabbath. His disciples were hungry, so they began to pick ears of corn and eat grain. When the Pharisees saw this, they said to Jesus, 'Look, it is against the law for your disciples to do this on the Sabbath.'

Jesus answered, 'Have you never read what David did that time when he and his men were hungry? He went into the House of God, and he and his men ate the bread offered to God, even though it was against the law to eat it.' As King David was one of their most revered ancestors the Pharisees could not continue the argument.

On another occasion the Pharisees planned to trap Jesus with a very clever question. They asked to whom should they pay homage, to God or to Caeser, the Roman Emperor. Jesus saw the trap. If he said 'to God,' he would have been in trouble with the Romans. But if he said 'To Caesar' then they would accuse him of speaking against God. Jesus asked them for a Roman coin. When they gave him one he held it up and asked, 'Whose face and name are on this coin?' They replied, 'The Emperor's.' So Jesus told them, 'Well then, pay the Emperor what belongs to him, and pay God what belongs to God.'

When they heard this the Bible tells us that the Pharisees were amazed — just as the priests and learned men had been amazed by the wisdom of Jesus as a twelve-year old boy.

God's Promises to Noah

made fun of Noah. 'What on earth is Noah doing?' they said. 'Why is he building a ship so far from any river or sea?'

The Bible tells us that God looked down upon the world, which He had newly created, and thought it was good. But soon things began to change. People started to disobey God. They were unkind to each other; they cheated each other; they quarrelled and fought. Their behaviour was so bad that God became very angry and decided that they must be punished. He would send a great flood which would drown everyone so that He could make a new start. Drown everyone, that is, except Noah and his family. God was pleased with Noah because he still lived a good life and followed God's laws. God told Noah what he planned to do but he promised him that he and his family would be safe.

God told Noah to build a huge boat called an ark. He gave Noah very careful instructions about how big it should be and how to make it. It had to be three storeys high and it would need a roof to keep out the rain. It had to have a window, a door and a number of separate rooms. It had to be painted with tar, inside and out, to make it watertight. Noah started on his massive task and slowly the ark began to take shape.

His neighbours were curious and they

Noah ignored them and carried on working. When the ark was finished, God had more instructions for Noah. God told Noah to collect one male and one female of every kind of animal God had created and put them into the ark.

Once they were all safely on board, and the door securely fastened, God made it rain. It rained and rained. It rained, as God had promised, for forty days and forty nights. The earth became so flooded that even the mountain tops were covered. But Noah, his family and his collection of animals were safe in the ark. All the other people and animals perished.

Eventually, the rain stopped and the flood water started to go down. The mountain tops reappeared. Noah sent out a raven but it didn't return. A few days later he sent out a dove which returned so quickly that Noah realised that it had not found anywhere to land. The next time Noah sent out the dove it returned with a twig which it had broken from a tree. Noah now knew that land must be near and the great flood was nearly over. A few days later the boat touched dry ground and Noah's family and the animals left the boat. God had kept his promise to keep them safe.

God then made His second promise. He created a beautiful rainbow which arched across the sky.

'Whenever you see a rainbow,' said God. 'Remember that I have promised never again to flood the earth. You know that I never break a promise.'

Abraham and Isaac

Any son or daughter, is precious to their parents but Isaac was that much more precious to Abraham and his wife Sarah because he was born when Abraham was one hundred years old and Sarah was ninety. It was only through God's intervention that this could happen. The parents were overjoyed when the son they had so longed for was born. Sarah said 'God has brought me great joy.'

The years passed and Isaac grew to be tall and strong. It was then that God decided to test Abraham's obedience.

God called to him, 'Abraham.' And Abraham answered, 'Yes, here I am.'

'Take your son,' God said, 'Your only son, Isaac, whom you love so much and go to the land of Moriah. There on a mountain that I will show you, offer him as a sacrifice to me.'

Abraham was stunned. How could God ask him to do such a dreadful thing? How could he ever explain Isaac's death to Sarah? Nevertheless, Abraham had learned to place complete trust in God and knew that he must obey. Next day it was with a heavy heart that Abraham cut some wood for the sacrificial fire, loaded his donkey with provisions, and set out with Isaac and two servants. On the third day Abraham saw in the distance the place God had told him about. He told the servants, 'Stay here with the donkey. The boy and I will go over there and worship, and then will come back to you.'

Isaac was told to carry the wood for the scarifice and Abraham carried a knife and the live coals for starting the fire. As they walked forward Isaac said, 'Father!'

'Yes, my son?'

'We have the wood and coals, but where is the lamb for the sacrifice?'

Abraham answered, 'God himself will provide one.'

When they reached the place for the sacrifice, Abraham built an altar of stones and placed the wood on top. He tied his son's wrists and legs together and placed him on top of the wood. Then holding the knife in both hands he raised it above his head.

Just as he was about to plunge it into his son God called, 'Abraham, Abraham.'

He answered, 'Yes, here I am.'

'Do not hurt the boy, or do anything to him. I now know how much you trust me and that you will always obey me.'

With trembling hands Abraham untied his son and lifted him off the altar. On God's instructions they found a ram in a nearby bush, caught by his horns. They killed it and roasted it as a sacrifice on the altar. It was then that God made three promises to Abraham and his people. He promised the Jews, that they would have a land of their own, that they would become a great nation and, that all the families on earth would be blessed.

Mohammed and the Angel

The Angel Gabriel who appeared to Mary to tell her she would give birth to Jesus also appeared to Mohammed, the man who was the great prophet of Islam. He gave Mohammed the laws God wanted the Muslims to obey. These laws are written in the sacred book of Islam call the Qur'an.

As a boy Mohammed had been orphaned and had lived first with his grandfather and then with his uncle. Though Mohammed was loved and cared for, he was not taught to read.

When he was a young man he lived among people who worshipped many idols. Mohammed rejected their religion and worshipped one, great God. He was faithful and very serious about his faith but he did not know he would play such an important part in it. Mohammed often escaped the noise and bustle of the busy market town by retreating to a cave on Mount Hira where he could pray.

The year that Mohammed was forty, he went there as usual to fast and pray during the month of Ramadan. It was there that the Angel Gabriel came to him in a vision.

The Angel said to Mohammed, 'Read!'

'I cannot read,' replied Mohammed who must have been terrified by the vision.

Then Gabriel put his arms around Mohammed and held him very tight until Mohammed thought he would faint. When Gabriel finally let him go he said, 'Read!'

'I cannot,' answered Mohammed.

Again the Angel hugged Mohammed long and hard. 'Read!'

'I cannot.'

Then the Angel hugged Mohammed once more and said. 'Read in the name of the Lord who createth man from a drop of blood! Read; and thy Lord is most generous, who teacheth man the use of the pen and teacheth him that which he knew not before.'

After the Angel Gabriel said this, Mohammed repeated the words and knew he would never forget them. From that moment Mohammed would have a power of language that he would use to teach the will of God to the people of Islam.

But standing in the cave of Mount Hira, Mohammed was afraid. He did not yet know the full meaning of the Angel's visit to him. When he was sure Gabriel was gone, Mohammed ran out of the cave towards home.

But the Angel Gabriel spoke to him again. 'Mohammed! You are the messenger of Allah!'

Mohammed looked up to see the Angel so huge that he filled the whole sky and Mohammed could not get away from the towering figure.

When Mohammed reached home he told his wife, Khadija, what had happened. Neither of them understood at the time what it meant. But before long, Mohammed would risk his life to teach God's law and Khadija would be his first convert to Islam.

Honi and the Long Sleep

The Talmud is the second sacred book of the Jews. The first is the Torah which sets down the laws of Judaism and consists of the first five books of the Old Testament. Jews spend a great deal of time studying the Torah and the Talmud in an effort to understand exactly what God wants people to do.

One of the stories from the Talmud is about a very pious man named Honi the Circle. He earned this name during a terrible drought. The people of the drought-stricken area knew him to be a good and godly man and they asked him to pray to God on their behalf and ask for rain. Honi prayed. Nothing happened. Then Honi drew a circle around himself and promised God he would not move from the circle until enough rain fell to supply the needs of the parched land and the thirsty people. And it rained. Ever after Honi was known as Honi the Circle.

Honi continued his life of the study of God's word. He was particularly interested in how the Jews must have felt when they returned to the Holy Land after many long years in exile. He would soon learn this first hand for God had plans for Honi.

One day when Honi was walking in the countryside he saw a farmer planting a carob tree. Honi asked him why he bothered to plant it because it took seventy

years for a carob tree to mature and give beans. The farmer replied that he harvested the fruits of the trees planted by his grandfather and father, so his descendents would harvest the fruit of this tree.

Honi walked on, thinking about the devotion of the farmer. He began to feel hungry and looked for a place out of the sun where he could rest and eat a little. He found a cool cave and settled himself inside. Suddenly he grew profoundly tired and fell into a deep sleep. Honi slept and slept and slept. Vines grew over the mouth of the cave and no one knew what had happened to Honi the Circle. Seventy years passed and then the land suffered another drought. The vine covering the cave died from lack of water and the sun shone in, warming and waking Honi. He had no idea he had slept so long.

Honi stretched and yawned and walked out into the sunshine. He was suprised to see a farmer harvesting beans from the carob tree he had just planted. The farmer was suspicious of the stranger and told him his grandfather had planted that particular tree.

It suddenly dawned on Honi that his sleep might have lasted a full seventy years.

He hurried off to find out what had happened to his family and friends. He asked strangers in the road about them and was told the son of Honi the Circle was dead but that his grandson lived nearby. Honi found the house of his grandson and knocked at the door. The grown man who answered the door did not believe the old man in ragged clothes could possibly be his grandfather, Honi the Circle. Honi was saddened by the fact that his grandson did not know him or believe him.

He wandered despondently to synagogue where a group of scholars were studying the Talmud and they invited the old man to join them. They were very surprised at his great knowledge but, like the grandson, they did not believe he was Honi the Circle. Honi was sadder still at the realization that no one believed his story. He knew, at last, what it must have felt like for his ancestors to return to the Holy Land after so long in exile, for he had been exiled by time. Honi wandered back to the cave where he had slept and asked God if he had not lived long enough. God answered Honi by giving him the long, peaceful sleep of death.

The Water Carrier

Religious stories often teach lessons and tell people how to behave towards one another. Many similar stories can be found in the literature of different religions. The basic ideas that people have about right and wrong are pretty much the same no matter who they are or what their religious beliefs. The Sikhs' story of the water carrier is like the story of the Good Samaritan that Jesus tells in the Bible. Both tell us that even our enemies are our brothers.

The Sikh Guru Gobind Singh and his men had been fighting against the Emperor's troops for weeks. Both sides had lost many men and the ones left standing had fought to the point of exhaustion. The battlefield was scattered with the bodies of the dead and wounded. The noonday sun beat down and the wounded cried out for water.

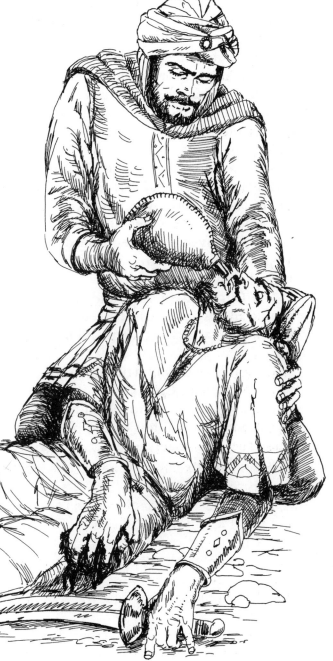

A man walked alone among the wounded. He stooped and gently lifted their heads, helping them drink water from a bowl he carried. He made no distinction between fellow Sikh and enemy. He gave water to who ever was wounded and thirsty.

Some Sikh soldiers who saw this reported the man to Guru Gobind Singh, telling him that the man was giving comfort to the enemy. The Guru sent the soldiers to bring the man to him.

The man's name was Bhai Ghanaya. When the Guru asked him if he had been giving water to friend and enemy alike, Bhai Ghanaya said, 'When I walk amongst the wounded I do not see friend and enemy, I only see people in need. Many are near death and surely a drink of water is not too much to share.'

The Guru was pleased and said, 'You should always help those in need, whoever they are. That is what a true Sikh would do.'

Then as Bhai Ghanaya turned to go back to the battlefield, Guru Gobin Singh gave him a jar of ointment and told him to use it to rub into the wounds of the people to whom he gave water, whether they were friend or enemy.

The Bloody Sword

On a lovely spring day, Guru Gobind Singh called his followers together to celebrate Baisakhi Day. He had set up a big tent on a hilltop and many people had answered his call and come. When a large crowd had assembled, the Guru went into the tent and came out again carrying a long, sharp sword.

Loudly he called to the people, 'Is there anyone here who would lay down his life for his God and his Guru?'

He looked around but no one came forward. He asked the same question again. No one could believe the Guru was asking someone to sacrifice himself. The Guru waited as if he were certain someone would step forward. Suddenly there was murmuring in the crowd and people stepped aside to let a man through. He stepped away from the others and walked to Guru Gobind Singh.

'I am willing to lay down my life for my God and my Guru,' he said.

The man and the Guru walked into the tent together. The crowd waited silently, wondering what would happen next. There was a terrible noise that sounded just like someone's head being lopped off! And the Guru reappeared carrying the sword. It seemed to be dripping with blood.

Without explanation the Guru said,

'Who will be next to lay down his life for his God and his Guru?'

Again there was some hesitation and again a volunteer came out of the crowd. He, too went into the tent with the Guru. The same terrible sound was heard. And the Guru returned with the sword freshly bloodied. The crowd of Guru Gobind Singh's devotees could not believe what they were witnessing. The Guru kept ask-

ing for people willing to lay down their lives for their God and their Guru until five in all had been taken into the tent. People began to flee in terror.

But the Guru called them back and many believed in him enough to listen. He disappeared into the tent for a sixth time and returned followed by all five men whom the crowd had feared were dead.

'These five trusted their God. They were willing to sacrifice themselves for him. As their reward they will be called the Blessed Five. All Sikhs should try to be like them.'

Then Guru Gobind Singh told the assembled people that these five would be the first of a Sikh brotherhood called the Khalsa. He said all devout Sikhs could belong to the brotherhood and that they would all share the same name. Men would all be called Singh, meaning lion, and women would all be called Kaur, meaning princess. He told the men they must never cut their hair but wear it twisted and fastened with a comb and covered by a turban wound around it. These, said the Guru, would be the distinguishing marks of Sikhs everywhere so all people would know who they were and that they were true and brave. So pleased were the people in the crowd with what the Guru had said that many thousands of them became members of the Khalsa on that Baisakhi Day and Sikhs all over the world still wear the turban and bear the names given them that day.

The Honey Pots

When Saul was the King of the Israelites, the city of Ascalon was ruled by the Philistines who were their enemies. Amongst the citizens of Ascalon there lived a beautiful and wealthy widow. One of the Philistine captains wanted to marry the widow because he had heard she was very rich. The widow decided to run away from her home and live elsewhere until it was safe to return. But what should she do with the fortune she had inherited from her husband? Her eye fell upon the huge, clay pots in her storeroom and they gave her an idea. She emptied the foodstuffs out of the pots and put all her gold and silver coins into them. Then she poured honey on top of the coins until the pots were brim full. It was impossible to see the coins beneath the rich, golden honey. Then she told her neighbour she was going away and asked him to watch over her pots of honey. He willingly agreed.

Not long after the widow had left Ascalon, the neighbour needed some honey. As he had none he decided to borrow some from the neighbour's pots, fully intending to replace it in the future. When he tipped out some honey, he realised there were coins below and greed overtook him. He emptied the pots of honey, took the coins for himself and refilled the pots with more honey.

Eventually, the Philistine captain died

and the widow was able to return to her home and to her pots of honey. In need of money, she emptied out the honey from the first jar, only to find her money was gone. The widow went to a judge and accused the neighbour of taking her money. The judge asked her if anyone had seen her put the coins into the honey pots. Of course, no one had because she had intended to keep her hiding place a secret. Where could the poor woman turn?

On the advice of the judge, she went to

King Saul with her problem. She told her story to the King and asked him to help. He asked her if she had any proof of the story she had told and she had to say again that she did not. 'Then,' said King Saul, 'I cannot help you.'

She left the court in tears of despair. Some young boys playing in the street saw how distressed she was and asked what was wrong. After she had told them her story one of the boys who was called David said, 'Don't despair. Go ask King Saul if he will let me help you prove your case.'

The widow went back to the King and asked if he would hear the boy's argument and the King agreed.

David bowed to King Saul and the King asked him how he could possibly prove what wise and learned judges found impossible to prove.

David answered, 'The outcome of the case rests in God's hands and I trust in Him.'

They returned to the widow's house and found the same pots the coins and honey had been in. The boy directed that the honey should be emptied out of them and then he smashed all the pots. Stuck to the honey on the inside of one of the shards were two coins.

'There,' said David, 'Is the proof of what the widow claims.'

King Saul and his judges and the neighbour had to admit that the boy and the widow were right. Little did they know at the time how great a king the boy David would grow up to be.

Faithful Ruth

Once, long ago in Israel, there was a terrible drought and poor harvests left many people hungry. Elimelech and his wife Naomi and their sons Mahlon and Chillion decided to move to the country of Moab where the drought was less severe. There they hoped to be able to plant and harvest a better crop.

They found that they could, indeed, grow their crops and they managed to make a good home for themselves in the new land. But their happiness was short-lived for Elimelech soon died and left Naomi a widow.

Naomi was a kind and considerate mother and thought of the happiness of her two sons. She urged them to marry and make families of their own. Mahlon and Chillion loved their mother and wanted to stay with her so that they could care for her, but they finally agreed to marry and sought Moabite wives. Chillion married a young woman named Orpah amd Mahlon married one called Ruth. The two couples were happy for a short time but once again tragedy struck. Both young men died, leaving their young wives widowed as well.

Naomi was very fond of her two daughters -in-law and they also of her. The three women lived together, helping and caring for each other. As Naomi grew older she longed to go home to Israel. She told Orpah and Ruth they should marry again and have children. Eventually, Orpah agreed and married a Moabite man. But Ruth steadfastly refused to leave Naomi. She promised to go with her mother-in-law to Israel and look after her. Ruth said, 'Your people will be my people and your God, my God.' And Naomi saw that she could not change Ruth's mind.

When they returned to the place Naomi had lived before, they found the drought was over so they were able to live there again. Many of the people who had known Naomi before remembered her and welcomed her back. They admired Ruth for her strength and learned to love her for the way she cared for her mother-in-law.

One of the ways poor people were able to get food was to follow labourers who were harvesting grain and pick up bits they dropped. It was called gleaning and landowners allowed people to do this. One of the landowners, a man called Boaz, was a distant relative of Naomi's dead husband and Ruth went to glean in his fields. Boaz noticed Ruth and was attracted to her. He told her she could glean his fields whenever she wanted and then he instructed his labourers to drop extra grain for Ruth to find.

There was a Jewish law at that time that said if a man died, his closest relative should marry his widow so she could remain part of the family. Naomi told Ruth that Boaz was related to her dead husband and that, if there were no closer relative, Boaz could marry Ruth. Naomi advised Ruth to ask Boaz his advice on the matter. Ruth was a bit shy about it but at the harvest festival she saw her chance to talk to Boaz.

Boaz wanted to marry Ruth but he knew there was a man who was a closer relative to her dead husband than he was. Boaz went to the man and asked him if he wanted to marry Ruth. The man already had a family and could not take on more responsibilities. He took off one of his sandals and handed it to Boaz. That was the traditional and symbolic way of giving Boaz his right to marry Ruth.

And so Ruth and Boaz were married much to the delight of Naomi. In time, they had a son named Obed. Obed grew up to become the grandfather of King David.

Marriages are Made in Heaven

The Queen of Sheba liked visiting King Solomon in Jerusalem. He liked telling her stories that showed how great God was. He told her of all the miracles God could perform. He told her that even things that seemed insignificant were important to God. The Queen doubted that a God as great as King Solomon's could be bothered with the lives of ordinary people. King Solomon assured her that He was. In fact, the King said, God even concerns himself with the right people finding and marrying each other. King Solomon told her that all marriages were made in heaven. The Queen of Sheba did not believe this. She challenged King Solomon to prove it.

When he asked her how, she made a suggestion.

The Queen said they should choose a young maiden and put her far from all other people. If King Solomon's God could find her a husband in that situation, then the Queen would have to believe what King Solomon had said.

So King Solomon and the Queen of Sheba went together through Jerusalem to look for a suitable maiden. When they found her, they asked her parents' permission to take her away and they paid them a great deal of money. The young woman was not sure she wanted to go but she had no choice. Her name was Penina.

King Solomon and the Queen of Sheba took Penina on a boat to a remote, island where there was one particularly big tree. In the very top of the tree they made a little house for Penina. She could not get out but there was one small window through which food could be passed to her every day. She was given some things to amuse her and there she was left for five years. The Queen of Sheba was sure that even a God as great as King Solomon's God could not make a match for Penina in that situation.

Each day a magic pheasant took food from the King's court to the little window and Penina took it from him. The bird was her only visitor. She was very lonely.

And while Penina was imprisoned in her tree house, a ship sailed nearby on its way to the Holy Land. A young man named Reuben was helping his father sail the boat when a terrible storm came up very suddenly. The waves were enormous and Reuben was washed overboard. His father thought he must have drowned but Reuben was able to get safely to shore. The shore was the island where Penina was. As Reuben hunted for food, he noticed the pheasant. He watched it fly to the tallest tree on the island. He watched with growing curiosity as it passed a parcel in the small window at the top of the tree. Something or someone, he thought, must be inside that tree.

Reuben climbed right to the top of the tree and called in the window. Penina was surprised and delighted to hear another human voice. They talked for a long time through the window. Penina told Reuben the story of how she came to be there. The pheasant flew to King Solomon to give him the news. Then he flew back to keep an eye on the two young people.

Reuben and Penina fell in love very soon. Reuben managed to enlarge the window in the tree so he, too could get into the tiny house. They decided to get married and the pheasasnt flew from King Solomon's palace with all that was necessary for a wedding feast. Then they settled down to live in the tree house because King Solomon had not yet decided it was time to tell the Queen of Sheba what had happened. He was saving it for a big surprise.

Time passed and Reuben and Penina had a baby girl whom they called Sheba because they knew if it hadn't been for the wager the Queen had had with King Solomon they never would have found each other.

Then it happened that the King's son was getting married. The Queen of Sheba would be attending the wedding festivities and the King decided it would be a very good time to tell her what had become of Penina. He was looking forward to seeing the look on her face when she found out what had happened.

But further joy was waiting for Reuben. A ship took him and Penina and baby Sheba to the court of King Solomon and on the journey he was by chance reunited with his father, who had never given up hope of finding his son alive.

As for the Queen of Sheba, she may have lost the wager but she was very pleased to see how King Solomon's great God had overcome all obstacles and led Reuben to Penina.

Being Buddhist

Buddhism is one of the major religions in the world but Buddhists do not believe in god. Some people think Buddhism is more a philosophy of life, a way of living, rather than a religion. Buddhists believe in and try to follow the teachings of a man called Siddhartha Gautama, who came to be known as Buddha.

Siddhartha Gautama was born about 2,500 years ago in Nepal, a country north of India. He was the son of a king and lived in great luxury in a beautiful palace. He had everything he wanted and servants to wait on his every wish. But Gautama was curious about what the rest of the world was like. One day he went to a nearby village and was appalled at the poverty and suffering of the people there. It was his first encounter with the kinds of lives people were living outside the palace walls.

Gautama could no longer enjoy his elegant lifestyle. He felt he had to understand why there was such suffering and find out if there was something that could be done about it. He left his father's palace and travelled into the next kingdom where no one knew him. Instead of his fine robes and jewellery he wore only beggar's clothes. He carried a begging bowl into which people could put morsels of food if they wanted to. He wandered from place to place, seeking out hermits and holy men, hoping to learn the answer to his burning question — was there any way to stop people's suffering? He could not find the answer in talking to other men.

Gautama grew more and more lonely. He was nearly starved and tired from his travels. One day he sat down beneath a bo tree and decided he would not move from the place until he had found the answer he sought. Gautama no longer looked to the world or other men for the answer. He closed his eyes and looked into himself. Gautama used a kind of deep thinking that has come to be called meditation. His thoughts were so deep he became completely unaware of anything around him. He concentrated only on what was inside himself. He entered into a state of perfect thought which came to be known as 'nirvana'. It was a state in which he wanted nothing. He could completely relax with his thoughts and just be.

When Gautama reached that enlightened state he was no longer Siddhartha Gautama. He became Buddha, which means the awakened or enlightened one. He would be known as such for the rest of his life and long beyond that.

Buddha then spent forty-five years wandering through northern India taking his message to anyone who would listen.

Buddha believed people could escape from suffering by following the Eightfold Path. The first of the eight principles is Right Seeing or Understanding and it means understanding what Buddha taught. Buddhists must first understand the main ideas of Buddhism before they can put them into practice in their own lives. The next seven steps help them to do that. They are Right Thought, Right Speech, Right Action, Right Livelihood, Right Effort, Right Mindfulness, Right Contemplation. These might sound a bit vague but Right Speech, for example, can mean not speaking in an unkindly way to anyone. Speaking harshly can hurt someone's feelings and that is a kind of suffering and Buddhists try never to cause anyone any suffering. Right Action means doing good things. Other religious teachings tell people to follow right action as well. The Ten Commandments from the Old Testament, for example, tell Christians what things to do and not to do and in that way teach what right actions are.

The principles of the Eightfold Path are not really laws or rules but ideas about how people should behave toward each other to make the world a better place so there is less suffering.

Buddha taught these ideas to people regardless of sex, age, class or race. Some of the people who heard him used his ideas in their daily lives. Others, however, changed their lives completely. They gave up all their worldly possessions and followed Buddha, teaching others what he had taught them.

Palm Sunday

Jesus and his disciples made their way to Jerusalem. As they walked they were joined by hundreds of other people travelling to the city to celebrate the Feast of Passover. This was a most important occasion for the Jewish people. The festival reminded them of the time when God had helped their ancestors escape from slavery in Egypt.

Everyone travelled looking forward to the celebrations and the knowledge that they were going to enjoy themselves. Everyone, that is, except Jesus. He was only too aware of what awaited him. He knew that in less than a week he would be crucified. He also knew that he must go through with the ordeal because that was his Father's plan. Only through his death could the sins of the world be forgiven.

Jesus turned to his disciples and gave them an order: 'Go to the village there ahead of you; as you go in you will find a donkey tied up that has never been ridden. Untie it and bring it here. If anyone asks you why you are taking it, tell him that the Master needs it.' They went on their way and found everything as Jesus had told them.

'Why are you untying it?' people asked.

'The Master needs it,' the disciples answered; and they took the donkey to Jesus.

They threw their cloaks on its back and helped Jesus to mount. Astride a donkey and surrounded by his disciples, Jesus entered Jerusalem. People suddenly realised who he was and they gave him a reception which was usually only given to kings. They threw their cloaks onto the roadway for Jesus to ride over. They chopped branches off the palm trees and spread them in front of him. Then the crowd

surged round him and started shouting. 'Hosanna! Blessings on him who comes in the name of the Lord! God bless the King of Israel.'

The Pharisees were worried and jealous. They could see that Jesus was very popular. Unless something was done about him he would take their place as leader of the people. They were even more determined to kill him. Jesus was taken prisoner and led before the Roman governor, Pontius Pilate.

A few days later it was the Feast of the Passover. On this day it was Pilate's custom to release one prisoner. He offered the crowd the chance for Jesus to go free. The people refused this offer, preferring instead the release of Barabus, a known murderer. 'What then, shall I do with Jesus called the Messiah?' Pilate asked the crowd. 'Crucify him! Crucify him!' they all chanted.

Jesus' popularity on the day he entered Jerusalem, which we now call Palm Sunday, leaves us with a puzzling question. How was it possible for this same crowd to turn against him only a few days later and demand his crucifixion? They had shouted, 'Hosanna! Blessings on Him who comes in the name of the Lord! God bless the King of Israel.' But within a few days these same people refused to save Jesus from death.

Part of the reason for this change of attitude towards Jesus was caused by the fact that the people had been waiting for a Messiah, or King for a long time. A Messiah who they hoped would save them. But not a Messiah who would save them from their sins but save them from the hated Romans who governed their land.

They were looking for a great military leader, a king who would raise a great army and drive the Roman army out of their country. They had probably imagined that their Messiah would enter Jerusalem riding a magnificent white horse and brandishing a flashing sword. But Jesus came on a donkey —a very humble animal. They couldn't imagine this Messiah being a great general. But it had been prophesied that Jesus, the Prince of Peace, would arrive on a donkey. 'Look, your King is coming to you. He is humble and rides on a donkey.'

He fulfilled the prophesy but the people's expectations of a war-like leader were dashed, and in their bitter and angry disappointment they savagely turned against Jesus.

Some Ideas about How the World Began

The book of Genesis in the Old Testament tells how God created the world and everything in it in six days and then rested on the seventh day. Each day He created another part of the world and on the sixth day He put man on the earth. This Judeo-Christian story of creation tells how God made the first man, Adam, from clay and how the first woman, Eve, was then made from one of Adam's ribs.

Many cultures have their own ideas about how the world was created and how people came to be. All of the stories tell about a time in the very far distant past. Most of these stories of creation are very, very old and were not written down for many generations. They were remembered and retold thousands of times by the descendants of the people who first told them.

Some ancient people in China told about a huge egg inside which there were the beginnings of everything that would ever be. Today scientists believe something similar to this idea might have occured when the universe was formed. It is called the 'Big Bang' theory. This theory sup-poses there was a huge ball of all matter in the universe tightly packed together. It supposes the ball exploded, scattering all that matter to make the millions of stars and planets. The Chinese idea of the cosmic egg is not quite so scientific but it is just as exciting. It tells of a creature called Phan Ku being born from the egg. He had horns and tusks and was covered with downy hair. From parts of himself he made the world and all the land forms and bodies of water. He made the sun and the moon and light and darkness. All the planets in the world came from his hair and the fleas that lived in the hair on his body became the people of the world.

In many of the other creation stories, people are made from clay or some other material and then brought to life by a god in the form of an animal or human. The Blackfoot American Indians believe the creator was 'Old Man' and that the first people he made were a woman and a child whom he formed of clay and then commanded to live. From some of the islands in the Pacific Ocean comes the story of Quat, who carefully carved jointed puppets from wood. He then did a sacred dance to bring them to life.

In other stories humans grow from plants. The Inuir people tell about the first man coming out of a pea pod. He dropped from the pod and was immediately fully grown but he knew nothing of the world and had to be looked after. A creator in the form of a raven looked after the new man and taught him about the world. The raven could change shape and become a man himself. He made other animals out of clay for the man's use and, in secret, he made a clay woman. The raven waved his wings over the clay figure and she came to life.

Some creation stories tell of mankind growing out of other creatures. Many stories that come out of Nordic traditions tell of giants and trolls and other partly human creatures. An Icelandic story of creation tells how the first two people grew from the armpit of an evil, sleeping ice giant. Later, the Nordic gods made the rest of the world from parts of his body. Ancient Egyptians believed people were created out of the tears of the sun god Ra.

In some myths of creation the creator was a man, in others she was a woman. The Huron Indians of North America believe the sky tore open and a woman fell toward earth. She was rescued by birds and a turtle. There was no earth and the woman had to make it. Animals were sent down into

the sea to bring soil up from the bottom. Several tried and failed but finally a toad was able to bring some soil up in his mouth. The woman spread the soil around the edge of the turtle's shell and that was the beginning of the earth.

Some West African people tell the story of Nana Buluku who was the first mother. She had twins called Mawu, the moon, and Lisa, the sun. They were to become the mother and father of all people.

In the Mayan story of creation, Heart of Sky, the Maker and the Feathered Serpent were a committee who created all things. They had only to think or speak the name of what they wanted to make and it was made. They tried three times to create living things as they thought they should be. They created the animals but were not satisfied because the animals could not speak. They created clay man but he could not move. They created wooden man who could move but who lacked soul. Then on the fourth try they created man. This man was able to do all the things the gods could do. But the gods thought this man was too good, so they took away some of his powers and made him just an ordinary human being.

All creation stories develop out of people's need to explain where they came from. How everything started is still a scientific mystery. It is very hard to imagine what there was before there was anything at all.

Death of a Pharaoh

There were thirty dynasties of pharaohs who ruled during 3,000 years of Egyptian history. During those centuries people's ideas about some things changed. But one thing that remained constant was the Egyptians' firm belief in the afterlife. They believed that when a person died he began a new life inside the earth where they thought the sun went after it set. They also believed that if they prepared a dead person properly, he would one day be reunited with his soul, or Ka, and live again.

Because life after death was so important to them, the Egyptians established huge burial areas. Each one of these was a city of the dead or a necropolis. Egyptians believed the sun died whenever it went down and was reborn every morning when it rose. And they believed that, like the sun, people would be born, die, and be born again. Because the sun rose in the east, they came to associate the east side of the River Nile with life. The sun went down in the west and so they came to associate that side of the River Nile with death. A dead person would always be buried on the west bank of the river.

Even the poorest people tried to preserve the dead bodies of their loved ones by burying them in the drying sand of the desert. They always buried with them a few essentials for life, such as food and tools. When a child died, toys were buried also. But when a pharaoh died, the preparations and ceremonies surrounding the burial were very elaborate and expensive.

Preparation for the burial of a pharaoh began long before he died. A pharaoh's tomb had to be huge and beautiful and it took many years to build. A few of the pharaohs were entombed inside enormous pyramids but many more were laid to rest in palaces carved into mountain sides. These palaces for the dead had many rooms and were richly decorated with carvings and paintings. The pharaoh himself would have overseen the construction of his tomb. It would have to be furnished with all the necessities and luxuries of his life at court. Golden furniture and a virtual army of statues of slaves and workers would be sealed into the tomb palace with him. The Egyptians believed the statues could be brought to life by certain prayers.

When the king was finally entombed, elaborate foodstuffs would be prepared and buried with him.

All the rules and ceremonies concerned with the preparation of a dead person for the afterlife are carefully laid down in The Book of the Dead. Any step left out or carried out wrongly would mean the dead person might never be reunited with his Ka.

When the pharaoh finally died, there were seventy days of preparations before he could be buried. Mummification of the body required all the skill of the high priests. Egyptians discovered mummification by accident when they found the desert sand could dry out and preserve

dead bodies. They went on to perfect the process using chemicals and embalming techniques. First, the high priest had to make a cut in the left side of the pharaoh's abdomen and remove his inside organs. These parts had to be carefully embalmed and stored in canopic jars. These were large earthenware jars that had the animal heads of some of the Egyptian gods sculpted on their lids. The pharaoh would

need his inner organs when he lived again. The heart was treated in a special way. Egyptians believed the heart was the centre of a person. They believed it was the seat of intelligence and the soul so they embalmed and wrapped it and put it back inside the body. The brains, however, were thought to be of little value. They were pulled out through the nose with a special hook and discarded.

The emptied body was packed in a drying chemical called natron. When it was dry, the elaborate wrapping with linen bandages began. The wrapping alone took many days and had to be very carefully and correctly done. The wrapped body was placed in several coffins, one inside the other. These were painted with heiroglyphic writing and the pharaoh's face was painted on the outer one. The coffins, or sarcophagi, might be covered in gold and decorated with precious stones. When the body was finally ready for burial, the next pharaoh had to perform the opening of the mouth. This was only a symbolic gesture because the pharaoh's mouth was well wrapped up inside many layers. A ceremonial tool like a lever was touched to the mouth of the portrait on the sarcophagus. The open mouth would allow the Ka to re-enter the body.

While priests were preparing the body of the dead man, they believed that the gods were putting his soul to a rigorous test. One of the more important Egyptian gods was the jackal-headed god Anubis. He had to escort the soul of the dead pharaoh to a hall of judgement. There the very important god, Osiris, sat as judge. Before the throne of Osiris was a balance scale. The pharaoh's heart was placed on one side of the balance and a feather on the other. A panel of lesser gods asked the dead person questions that he had to answer truthfully. These were questions such as, 'Have you ever told a lie?' or 'Have you ever killed anyone?' If the pharaoh had always done the right thing and did not lie when he was questioned, his heart would prove to be as light as the feather and he could go on to happiness in the after life. If, however, he had not led a good life, there was a monstrous beast waiting to devour his heart. The beast had the head of a crocodile, the mane and body of a lion and the haunches of a hippopotamus. Egyptians dreaded that beast because without a heart, the dead could never live again. If the pharaoh passed the test, he could pass into the Fields of the Blessed and all the earthly preparations surrounding his death would not have been in vain.

Jesus Appears to his Disciples

After the Crucifixion, when Jesus had died on the cross, two men were leaving Jerusalem to return to their homes in Emmaus. They were both followers of Jesus and were very upset. As they discussed everything which had happened they were caught up by a stranger.

'Why are you looking so sad?' the stranger asked.

'Are you the only one in Jerusalem who doesn't know what has happened there during the last three days?' said one of the men.

'Why, what has happened?' the stranger inquired.

'Jesus has been crucified. He was our leader. He was a great teacher. We thought he was God's son, the one the prophets have promised would come as our King and free us from our enemies. Then this morning some of our friends went to his tomb and found that his body had gone.'

'Why are you so puzzled?' the stranger asked. 'Don't you know that the prophets also said that this would happen?'

The man told them of all the occasions when the prophets, going all the way back to Moses, had foretold that the Messiah was bound to suffer, before he could rise from the dead and rejoin his Father in Heaven.

By this time they had reached the village of Emmaus. The stranger made as if to continue on his journey but they asked him, 'Stay with us, for the evening draws on, and the day is about over.' So he went into the house with them.

When they sat down at the table for supper, he took the bread and said the blessing. Then he broke the bread, and offered it to them. Suddenly they realised that the stranger was in fact Jesus. At that moment,

Jesus vanished from their sight.

The two men discussed what had happened. 'Did we not feel our hearts on fire as he talked with us on the road and explained the scriptures to us?' they said.

Later that same evening the disciples and some of their friends were sitting together inside a locked room. The shutters over the windows were fastened and the doors securely locked. They were afraid that the High Priest might send his men to arrest them as they were the followers of Jesus.

Suddenly, Jesus was standing in the room with them. At first they were terrified. How had Jesus entered a locked room? They thought they were seeing a ghost. Jesus knew what they were thinking. 'Touch me,' he said. 'Ghosts aren't made of flesh and bones.' They were beginning to believe it really was Jesus.

Jesus asked, 'Have you anything to eat?' They gave him some fish and watched him eat it. After that there were no more doubts. Ghosts don't eat. It was Jesus! He was real! He was alive!

Jesus explained to them how all that had happened was part of God's plan. He quoted the prophets and from the psalms. 'God's King had to suffer and die,' he said, 'And rise from the dead. The penalty for sin has been paid. Death has been conquered. Now God offers a free pardon to everyone who believes in him and comes to him ready to start a new life.'

The Hindu God Vishnu

The Hindus worship many gods. The god Vishnu is the most popular of them. Many people worship Vishnu and believe his presence is everywhere. Vishnu takes on many forms and changes his appearance whenever he needs to. In the great Hindu book called the Bhagavad Gita, Vishnu says he will always be ready to appear on earth to defend faithful Hindus from injustice, punish sinners amd make sacred laws. There are many stories about Vishnu and one of them is a little like the Bible story of Noah and the Ark.

Surya, god of the sun, had a son called Manu. One day Manu was washing himself in the river. He scooped the refreshing water in his hands and splashed it over his body and face to wash away the dust. He scooped a double handful of water and was about to pour it over his head when he noticed that he had scooped up a tiny fish in the water.

The fish spoke to Manu and said, 'Please save me! Big fish will eat me if I stay in the river.'

Manu took the little fish home, put it into a jar and looked after it. The little fish grew and was soon too big for the jar. Manu had promised to keep the fish safe so he dug a pond for it to live in. The fish continued to grow and was soon too big for the pond.

The fish told Manu he was called Matsya and he said, 'Take me to the great ocean.'

Manu did what Matsya told him to do. They reached the ocean and before Matsya swam away he spoke to Manu again. He said, 'In a year there will be a great flood. Build a ship and when the flood comes, take refuge in it. Then I will come to you again.'

Again Manu did what the fish told him to do and he prayed to Matsya every day for he now knew that this was no ordinary fish.

When the flood waters began to rise his boat floated safely. Soon Matsya appeared to Manu from the deep, dark flood waters. He had grown even bigger and had gleaming golden scales and a horn on his nose.

'Tie your ship to my horn and I will tow you safely through the flood waters,' said Matsya.

The storm that brought the flood continued to rage and the seas rose and covered the land and every living thing except Manu and Matsya was drowned. Matsya towed Manu's ship to the high peaks of the Hemavat mountain. This was the only part of the world that stuck up above the flood waters. Matsya told Manu to tie his ship to the peak and wait for the flood waters to go down.

Then Matsya said, 'I am the great god Vishnu. I have appeared to you as a fish to save you from the flood. You alone have been saved and you must create new people and animals and plants to live after the flood is over.'

Then Vishnu vanished and Manu never saw him again because Vishnu slept for millions of years before he appeared again.

God and Jonah

There is a story in the Old Testament about a man called Jonah. He was a good man and God decided to ask him to go to a terribly wicked city called Nineveh and deal with the people there. They had not been living good lives and God wanted Jonah to go and tell them to mend their ways and live according to God's laws.

When God spoke to Jonah and told him what He wanted him to do, Jonah was very frightened. He was afraid to go to such a wicked place and he was very worried about what the lawless people there would do to him if he started telling them what to do.

Instead of going to Nineveh as God asked him to, Jonah decided to run away. He quickly packed his things and went to the port to find passage on a boat. He wanted to get as far from God as he could. Of course, it isn't possible to run away from God for He is everywhere but Jonah tried.

As the boat slipped out of port, Jonah hid below decks so God would not see him. Of course, God knew exactly where Jonah was and what he was doing. When the boat was far from land, God sent a terrible storm to toss and tear at the boat. All the people on board were very frightened. Jonah knew God had sent the storm to punish him and he told the other people on the boat what God was doing. The sailors threw Jonah into the water. Immediately, the sea became calm. God was pleased. But he was not finished with Jonah yet.

As Jonah floated all alone in the vast ocean, a whale swam up to him. It opened its huge mouth and swallowed Jonah whole. Poor Jonah found himself imprisoned in the belly of the whale. While he was sitting in there, he began to think of how foolish he had been. He thought about God and how powerful He was. Jonah realized that he should have done what God told him to do. He felt sorry for the way he had disobeyed God and he wished he had another chance. God was pleased with Jonah's change of heart. But He still was not finished with Jonah.

The whale swam close to the land and opened its mouth. Jonah was thrown out onto the land. And he found himself quite close to the dreaded city of Nineveh. He knew what God wanted of him and he was now no longer afraid to do God's bidding. Jonah set out for Nineveh to do God's work.

Zarathustra

Once upon a time in ancient Iran there was a powerful magician called Durasan. He was the chief of all the magicians in that kingdom. One night Durasan had a disturbing dream. He dreamed that a child would be born who would grow up to destroy all magic, sorcery and idol worship.

When Durasan awoke he remembered the dream and believed that what he had dreamed would indeed come true. So Durasan and some other magicians set out for the city of Azarbijan where the dream had told him the child would be born. The magicians learned that the baby had been born into a wealthy family called Spitama and that he had been named Zarathustra. The magicians were determined to kill the child before the prophesy of the dream could come true.

The magicians took the child and tried to destroy him. All their efforts were thwarted. They built a huge fire and put the baby in the flames. But Zarathustra only played with them. He seemed unaware of the heat and was unharmed. The magicians put Zarathustra in the path of stampeding cattle. The first beast stopped and stood over the baby, protecting him from the rest of the herd. Durasan and his companions were beginning to feel desperate. They took the baby to a cave where wolves lived and put him amongst the hungry beasts. But the wolves could not get near Zarathustra and once again he came away unhurt.

The wicked magicians tried many other ways of disposing of the charmed baby but to no avail. Zarathustra grew up safe from all his enemies. When he was old enough to leave home, his parents sent him to learn the art of healing. He was an able student and learned his lessons well. He ministered to the poor and sick. As he worked among the people and saw their suffering he wondered about the forces that ruled peoples' lives. He thought hard about good and evil, about health and sickness, about joy and sorrow, light and darkness, life and death.

Zarathustra began to wonder if there was any way to drive evil out of the world. He decided he needed time to concentrate on this and nothing else. He decided to go to the hills and to live alone as a hermit.

For a long time he thought very hard and had nearly given up believing he would be able to find the answer to the question he had asked himself when he suddenly remembered something he had known all his life. That was that good only comes from good and evil only comes from evil. He realized it was impossible for good to ever come from evil. He came to the conclusion that the world was created from two forces, the God of Good and the God of Evil. Zarathustra thought the God of Good was responsible for purifying fire, cleansing water, fertile earth and fresh air. The God of Evil, he decided, made sickness, pestilence, pain and death. All of these things were in the world. But Zarathustra did not think it always had to be that way. He believed that if men worked hard for the God of Good, together they could overcome the God of Evil and make the world a better place. This idea became known as Dualism and this is what Zarathustra taught his followers.

Rama and Sita

The Ramayana is an epic tale from India. It tells the long and detailed story of the fate of a man called Rama who was destined to become a good and powerful king.

If Rama could tell his own story, he might do it like this:

I am Rama, the King of Ayodhya. I had to endure a great deal to become King. Dasaratha, the late King of Ayodhya was my father. He prayed to Vishnu, the creator and destroyer god for more good and less evil in his kingdom. The great god Vishnu answered his prayers by sending him four sons, myself (Rama), Lakshmana, Bharata, and Satrughna. We four brothers had shares of Vishnu's powers in relation to our age. I had the most and my brother Satrughna the least.

My brother Lakshmana and I were close friends and we spent our time fighting the demons and Ravana, the demon king, in all the kingdoms of the land. On our journeys we came across the kingdom of a man called Janaka.

Janaka was holding a competition of strength for young men to win the hand in marriage of his beautiful daughter, Sita. The test was to shoot an arrow from the mighty bow of the powerful goddess, Shiva. I stood by and watched as many princes tried to pull the enormous bow but all of them failed. The task looked impossible but I loved Sita at first sight and knew I must try.

I gathered up all my strength, pulled the great bow and fired the arrow. I had succeeded in winning Sita's hand and we were married immediately. Lakshmana, Sita, and I went back to live in Dasaratha's kingdom.

My father was growing old and he decided he would like to see me as king before he died. He made all the arrangements for my crowning and everyone was happy at the prospect because they loved and trusted me as they had my father.

But Kaikeyi, mother of my second youngest brother Bharata, wanted her only son to be king. Many years before, Kaikeyi had saved Dasaratha's life in battle and she was given two wishes as reward. She had saved these two wishes until the day when she might need them. When my father decided to make me king she told him she wanted her two wishes. The first wish was that her son Bharata be made king. The second wish was that I be sent away into exile in the forest for fourteen years. Dasaratha was a man of honour and he granted the two wishes because they had been promised.

I thought when I left Ayodhya I would have to leave Sita, my beloved and faithful wife. But she refused to stay behind and insisted on joining me in exile. My faithful brother, Lakshmana, came too.

The three of us were forced to go far away, deep into the forest, where we lived in a rough dwelling. Lakshmana and I continued to fight Ravana and his demons.

One day when Lakshmana and I were hunting in the forest we saw a deer running swiftly through the undergrowth. Thinking of meat we followed it and it led us very far away in the chase. When we finally got back to our dwelling we found the door standing open and my beloved Sita was gone!

We realized Ravana had tricked us into leaving Sita alone and he had kidnapped her. I was extremely angry but Lakshmana comforted me and we gathered our armies and set about finding Sita. As Sita was a clever woman, she had left a trail of her jewelry and some of her clothing for us to follow. The trail took us all the way down to the tip of India the land of Sugriva, the monkey king.

We had to cross the water to Sri Lanka.

King Sugriva had an intelligent and faithful follower who was Hanuman, or Son of the Wind. Hanuman gathered all his monkey friends together and they formed a bridge of monkeys for our armies to cross so we could get to the island of Sri Lanka.

On Sri Lanka we fought a long battle against Ravana and his demons. We had the help of Jambavan, the King of the Bears, as well as King Sugriva. But Ravana sent his son Indrajit into battle against us. Indrajit was ruthless. He made himself invisible and rode an invisible chariot out of the sky at us, armed with terrible weapons. He cut down all my allies and left us all for dead. Thanks to Hanuman, I am able to tell you this story now. Good Hanuman went as fast as the wind to the Himalaya mountains to find magical, medicinal herbs that brought me back to life. I was able to continue my battle with Ravana. At the end only Ravana and I were left. Even my faithful brother Lakshmana had been killed. Ravana and I fought hand to hand to the death. Finally, after a long struggle I triumphed.

I looked up and saw Sita running toward me with open arms. I wondered if I had been betrayed. Could Sita have been unfaithful to me with Ravana? She had been gone so long that I wasn't sure I could still trust her. I was torn between loving her and doubting her. When I told Sita this, she was very distressed. She made a huge pyre and laid herself upon it. She lit it and prepared to die to prove her faithfulness to me. Just in time the god of fire, Agni, came and blew the pyre out and scolded me for not trusting Sita. I begged Sita's forgiveness and she gave it to me.

Sita and I travelled back to Ayodhya. When we arrived, my brother, King Bharata, realised that I was the one brother worthy of being king so he handed the kingdom over to me. Sita and I were overjoyed and ruled for 10,000 years.

The Pharaoh and the Plagues

When Moses was a very old man, he was alone in the hills tending some sheep that belonged to his wife's father. He held a long stick in his hand — the kind shepherds used when tending their flocks. Suddenly before him there was a bush that burned brightly but did not burn away. It was not even scorched by the fire that burned in its branches. Moses could not understand what was happening. Then a voice came from the bush. It told Moses to take off his sandals because he was standing on holy ground. Then Moses understood that this was the voice of God.

The Lord God Jehovah told Moses of a promised land where the Israelites, who were slaves in Egypt, could go to live in peace and worship their god, Jehovah. But Moses did not see how the Israelites could go there while they were captive slaves in Egypt.

God asked Moses what he held in his hand and Moses answered that he held a shepherd's rod. God told him to throw it down onto the ground. Moses did as God commanded and the rod changed into a living snake. Moses turned to flee from the creature but God told him to pick it up. When he did, the snake turned back into a rod. Then God told Moses to go with his brother Aaron to the court of the Pharaoh and show him the miracle of the rod so Pharaoh would know about the power of the God of the Israelites.

First, Moses and Aaron went to Pharaoh and asked him to release the Israelites from bondage and let them go to the promised land. Pharaoh refused and sent them away.

Moses and Aaron went to Pharaoh a second time. This time, Aaron threw the rod down and showed Pharaoh how their God could change it into a serpent. Pharaoh was not impressed, however. He sent for the court magicians and they, too, had rods that could change into serpents. But the serpent from the rod Moses and Aaron had brought ate up all the other serpents. Then Aaron lifted it by the tail and it became the rod again.

Pharaoh still did not believe in the power of Jehovah and refused to let the Israelites go.

Next Moses and Aaron waved their rod and, with the help of Jehovah, turned all the waters of the Nile into blood. But Pharaoh's magicians did the same and Pharaoh said he did not fear the God of the Israelites.

Then Moses and Aaron waved their rod again and a plague of frogs came out of the river. There were frogs by the thousands. They went everywhere. Pharaoh's magicians could do the same but by now Pharaoh was a bit frightened of the power of Jehovah. He said, yes, the Israelites could go if Moses and Aaron could get rid of the frogs. They did but when the frogs had gone Pharaoh was no longer afraid and he went back on his promise and said the Israelites could not go after all.

So Aaron and Moses used the rod again and brought forth a terrible plague of insects to Pharaoh's lands. The magicians could do nothing like that and Pharaoh once again was afraid. But he would not give in and let the Israelites go to the promised land. Day after day Moses and Aaron went to Pharaoh and brought forth a new and terrible plague. Pharaoh stood fast and refused to let the Israelites go.

Finally, God said he would come to Egypt Himself and convince Pharaoh to let His people go. He told the Israelites what they must do to be safe from the last plague he would send. He told them to kill lambs for the last supper they would be eating in Egypt. He told them to smear the blood of those lambs on the doors of their houses. They had to do this as a sign to keep the plague away from their own houses for God was going to kill the firstborn son of every household in Egypt — unless it had blood on the door. So the Israelites smeared lambs' blood on their doors and the plague passed them by and killed only the firstborn sons of the Egyptians. Finally, Pharaoh was convinced that Jehovah, God of the Israelites, wanted his people to be free to go to the promised land. And Pharaoh let them go.

The Israelites had a long, difficult journey but God guided them by sending a pillar of smoke by day and a pillar of fire by night. And so the Lord God Jehovah led the Israelites out of Egypt.

PRAYERS

Peace Prayer

(Satish Kumar, a member of the Jain community. Adopted by the Prayer for Peace movement, 1987)

Lead me from death to Life,
from falsehood to Truth.

Lead me from despair to Hope,
from fear to Trust.

Lead me from hate to Love,
from war to Peace.

Let Peace fill our hearts,
our world, our universe.

Anger

(Adapted from a Chinese saying)

I was angry when I had to wear glasses,
  but then I met a man who was blind.
I was angry when I broke my leg,
  but then I met a boy who had been crippled since birth.
I was angry when I wasn't listened to,
  but then I met a girl who was deaf.
I was angry when I had no shoes,
  but then I met a man who had no feet.

Dear God, Love from Andrew

Thank you for being there when I needed you, God, and for looking after me when I came off my bike. Help me to try not to be so stupid in future, riding without my crash helmet on and dashing across the road, without looking, to see my friends. Maybe next time you won't be looking and I will be very badly injured. Please help my friends to learn from what might have happened to me. I'll try to do better, God, but I do need your help and guidance, and I pray you will always be there when I need you, as you were the other day. Thank you for my life, God. — Love from Andrew.

Arabic Prayer

It is glory enough for me
That I should be your servant.
It is grace enough for me
That You should be my Lord.

The Love of Christ

Vaster far than any ocean,
deeper than the deepest sea
is the love of Christ my Saviour,
reaching through eternity.

138

The Ten Perfections

(A Buddhist prayer)

I shall seek to develop the perfection of generosity, virtue, doing without, wisdom, energy, forbearance, truthfulnes, resolution, love, serenity.

Help Me to Love Myself and Others

Dear Lord, help us to make the best of what we have, and not to feel envy of others who may appear to have more than we do. Show us by your guidance how we can help those people worse off than ourselves by making what to us would only be a very small sacrifice. And most of all, Lord, help us to feel good about ourselves, no matter how we may look, for what clothes we wear or what we can do or can't do. We are all your children, and are grateful so to be.

Indian Prayer

(Yayurveda)

O Lord, give me strength that the
   whole world
looks to me with the eyes of a friend.
Let us ever examine the other with the
   eyes of a friend.

FICTION

Giving and Getting

I'm no angel. And I'm not rich. But I reckon there are people worse off than me and maybe I can do a little something for them. So after school every Wednesday I go along to the Old Peoples' Home. Our school arranged it, and several of us go, and we each visit a different person. Mine is Miss Beecham. I really like her. I think I'm the only person who comes to see her regularly. She has a nephew and he has a wife and two boys but they never come. I go to school with the boys. They know I

visit Miss Beecham because every Wednesday, no matter what, when I leave her, she always gives me fifty pence to buy them sweets. Every Thursday the two of them come running up to me before school. 'Have you been to see the old lady? Where are our sweets?' They don't even call her aunty. They don't care at all about her, but she never forgets them. It doesn't seem fair.

I like visiting the old people's home. Some of us take our pets along sometimes. The people there love that. My hamster is not happy about going in a box on the back of my bicycle but once I unpack him and hand him over to Miss Beecham for her to stroke, he calms down. The first time she saw him I thought she was going to have a heart attack. She thought he was a rat. Now she's used to him and loves to feed him bits of bread crust. She saves them in her pocket from her lunch. He saves them in his pouch for his supper.

I'm sort of Miss Beecham's errand boy. If she needs anything at the shops I get it for her so I know she never forgets to send a card and a present to that nephew or his family for birthdays, wedding anniversary, whatever. She never misses. She hasn't got much money at all. She digs into the pocket of her flowered frock and hands me whatever she has managed to save up and asks me to do the shopping for her. I have to buy the present and wrap it and deliver it. They don't even tell me to say 'Thank you' to her. Sometimes they make fun of the things she sends: 'Oh, brilliant! Another stupid scarf.' Or 'I hate this kind of chocolates!' And they never, never send

her anything. It makes me furious.

It was coming up to Christmas. I knew Miss Beecham would be asking me to get them presents. I didn't think I could do it. I was just so angry at them. Hey, I thought, that's not the Christmas spirirt. Go along and have a word with the nephew. It took a lot of nerve but I did it.

'Your Aunt would really like to have a visit or a present from you this Christmas. She's very kind. She's going to give you all presents and I thought you might like . . .' That's as far as I got. They said I was just being nosey. Mind my own business — that's what I should do. Leave the old lady alone.

Well, I wasn't going to leave the old lady alone and I'd got into this thing and I was going to finish it off.

The next Wednesday when I got to the

Home Miss Beecham had been waiting anxiously. She had big plans. She reached into her pocket.

'Now, David, it's coming up to Christmas and I've saved up thirty pounds . . .'

Thirty pounds! I couldn't stand it.

'Miss Beecham, I'm going to tell you something you don't want to hear. It's going to make you angry but I think you need to hear it.' I said. No turning back now. 'You never forget your nephew and his family. You send them sweets every week. You never forget their birthdays or anything. But they don't care about you at all. They just take things from you and they never even give you a minute's thought!' There, I'd said it and I felt awful.

Miss Beecham was quiet. I thought she might cry. 'I know you are right,' she finally said in a quiet voice. 'I think our visit is over for today. But don't forget me next Wednesday, will you.'

How could I. She was my Wednesdays.

One thing began to worry me. Did she think I was angling for a thirty pound present myself? I'd never expected her to give me anything. I hoped she knew me well enough to know that. I like getting presents as much as the next person but Miss Beecham was my chance to give and I liked it like that.

Wednesday came. I had decided how to say no to a thirty pound present in the nicest possible way, just in case. Miss Beecham was her usual sunny self. I took off my hat, coat, gloves, scarf and piled them on the end of her bed. I told her about the snow that had begun to settle. She interrupted.

'Is there still an Oxfam shop in the High Street?' she asked.

'Yes,' I said.

'Can you stop there on your way home?'

'Yes, easily.'

She reached into her pocket and took out a card and three ten pound notes.

'I thought about what you said,' she said. 'And I think you are right. I have decided to give my nephew a gift and a lesson. Read this.'

I took the card and read it. It said: A gift of thirty pounds has been given to Oxfam in your name. Merry Christmas.

We looked at each other. We smiled. And then we laughed. Great!

'Will you please take this to the Oxfam shop on your way home?' She handed me the thirty pounds. It was the most money I had ever held. Miss Beecham really trusted me. It felt great. 'And just pop this card through my nephew's door, will you?'

The Traffic Jam

Ivor Tully was a rag and bone man. He went round with his horse and cart to all the houses in town and collected everything that people had no further use for, and sold them to a scrap merchant. Ivor Tully did quite well at this. Every day, come rain or shine, you would see him with his horse and cart trudging from street to street calling out, 'Rag an' bones, Rag an' bones!' at the top of his voice.

Ivor Tully's horse was called Pugh and he was getting pretty old. His bones stuck out, and his teeth were yellowing, and his hairy old coat looked as though it didn't fit him very well. And of course, he didn't move very quickly any more. In fact, on some mornings he didn't feel much like going to work at all, especially if it was cold and dark outside. But Ivor wouldn't let him lie in.

'Come along with you,' he'd say. 'There's lazy you are. Don't you want to go out and see what the world is doing today?' Old Pugh would shake his shaggy head as if to say that he didn't expect the world would look any different this morning and he'd much rather stay in his warm stable and doze.

One cold winter morning Ivor took old Pugh out into the yard and harnessed him into the cart. It was very frosty and old Pugh's breath puffed out in clouds and formed dew on his velvet nose. Ivor put a blanket over his back, which made him feel slightly better, and they clip-clopped out into the street.

Now today turned out to be a good day for a rag and bone man. Mrs Francis gave them a roll of old lino. Mrs Evans gave them an old arm chair. Mrs Thomas gave them two old saucepans. Mrs Jones gave them an old brass bed . . . and a mattress . . . and a hideous vase . . . and a box of old china . . . and a rusty lawn mower . . . and . . .

The cart was getting heavier and heavier. Old Pugh was getting more and more tired. He could hardly move the cart at all when out came Mr and Mrs Jones again with their old gas cooker.

'Hold on a minute, Ivor. You might as well take this too.' Ivor Tully's eyes shone with joy. In his mind he was counting up all the money he would get for this junk. It was the best load he had had for weeks! Mr Jones helped him lift the gas cooker up onto the cart. Old Pugh started to pull . . . then something dreadful happened. Old Pugh's legs gave way! He sank to his knees. The cart tipped with him, and lino, beds, chairs, pots and pans and all kinds of junk fell clattering all around him. Some of it actually bounced off Pugh as it fell, but he didn't care. He just didn't care about anything anymore.

Ivor stood in the road in dismay. 'Whatever's the matter, Pugh? Get up this minute!'

Pugh shook his head dejectedly. Along came David Davis the policeman.

'What's going on here, Ivor Tully? Get this mess shifted, please. You are obstructing the highway, not too mention the pavement.'

'I will. I will,' spluttered Ivor. 'As soon
as my horse stands up.'

Pugh shook his head again. Along came
a big white police car.

'You havin' a bit of bother, Davis?' asked
the sergeant in the police car.

'No. No, Sarge.' replied David Davis,
trying to sound efficient. 'I shall have it
moved just as soon as the horse stands
up.'

Old Pugh shook his head again. He was beginning to enjoy himself. A huge lorry came down the road. The lorry driver climbed out of his cab.

'What's going on here? I'm in a hurry! I can't get by with all this junk in the road.'

'Just a second, sir,' said the sergeant. 'Constable Davis is handling it.'

'Just a second, Sarge,' said David Davis. 'Ivor Tully is handling it.'

'Just be a second,' said Ivor Tully. 'As soon as my horse stands up.'

Old Pugh shook his head. What a lot of people had gathered to watch. What an interesting day it had turned out to be.

'Poor thing,' somebody said. 'No wonder he laid down if he was expected to pull that load. It's downright cruelty to animals!'

Old Pugh nodded his shaggy head. At this point, lorry driver, sergeant, policeman and Ivor Tully started getting a bit angry. More and more traffic was building up behind the lorry. Car horns were hooting, people were shouting and old Pugh just sat and enjoyed it all.

'I suggest,' boomed Constable Davis in his loudest voice, 'you move this stuff onto the pavement, take your horse home and return with a hand barrow and clear it as fast as you can, Mr Tully!' Then, turning to the crowd he shouted, 'Move along please! Move along!'

The crowd began to move, muttering to themselves remarks such as, 'Poor animal!' 'Never should be allowed!' 'Taken for grantred!' 'Tut! Tut! Tut!'

Gradually, the people moved away. The police car drove off, the lorry eased past the pile of junk and the traffic jam slowly sorted itself out. Ivor Tully piled his junk as neatly as possible along the pavement . . . and Pugh stood up!

Old Pugh was pleased with himself. He had enjoyed the traffic jam immenseley.

Ivor Tully spent the rest of the day pushing his hand cart back and forth loaded with his junk. By teatime he was so tired that he fell asleep in his armchair before Mrs Tully gave him his tea, and as she put it back in the oven to keep warm she said to herself, 'Silly old man. Always did take that horse for granted.'

The Riddle

Michael McManus was miserable and miserly and never had a kind word to say to anyone. He lived all alone in his grey miserable cottage in Ireland and all day long he did his chores in a miserable grumpy way and every evening he sat and moped in front of his miserable empty fireplace.

'Why am I so miserable and lonely?' he moaned to himself one evening.

Much to his surprise a voice replied 'Because you are a miserable old miser who never enjoys anything. And there sitting on the back of his armchair was a little leprechaun. Michael blinked his eyes. Was that a real Irish leprechaun sitting there on the back of the his chair? He reached over and poked the leprechaun to see if he was real.

'Ouch!' said the leprechaun.

'You're a real leprechaun!'

'I am,' agreed the leprechaun. 'And it's not polite to poke people like that.'

'What do you think you are doing sitting there on my chair without being invited?'

'You did invite me. You said, "Why am I so miserable and lonely?" and that's an invitation if ever I heard one.'

'I don't invite people into my house,' grumbled Michael.

'Of course you don't. And that's why you are miserable and lonely. Your Happy Battery has run down and it's all rusty as well.'

'Rubbish!' said Michael. 'Whoever heard of a Happy Battery! Absolute rubbish!'

'Perhaps you never had one to start with Can you remember ever being happy in your young days?'

'I've always been old,' grumbled Michael.

'Hmm. Going to be quite difficult then,' said the leprechaun.

'What is?'

'Charging up your Happy Battery. You will have to want it quite badly, you know.'

'Go away, you stupid little leprechaun. I haven't got time to waste on such silly nonsense.'

'Alright!' replied the leprechaun. 'I'll be off then. There are plenty of people who will appreciate my help. I'll say "Good day" to you then, Michael McManus.'

The little leprechaun stood up on the back of the chair and slowly began to disappear.

'Wait a moment! Don't go. I *would* like to be a little less miserable.'

'Alright, then. You have to be prepared to do a little work towards it yourself, mind. You have to find the answer to a riddle. Here it is. Write it down.' Michael got an old stub of pencil and a tatty envelope and began to write down the riddle.

'Look for something in lilies white
Look for something in owls at night
Look for something in violets blue
The clue is in everything that you do.'

By the time he had finished writing all this down the little leprechaun had completely vanished.

Michael read the riddle over and over again and it meant absolutely nothing to him, so in the morning when he went to the village he asked the postman.

'You do a lot of reading, all those envelopes and things. Can you understand this?' and he showed the envelope to the postman.

'The only thing that I can see is that lilies begins with an L.' and the postman got on his bike and went on his way. Michael underlined L and went on to Mrs O'Riley's shop.

'Two rashers of bacon and an egg,' said Michael. 'And do you know anything about this?' He handed Mrs O'Riley the grubby envelope.

'I'm not much good at riddles, Michael,' she said, 'but if lilies begins with an L then "owls" begins with O.'

'I suppose so,' agreed Michael and he paid for his bacon and egg without even groaning about the price.

'Amazing!' said Mrs O'Riley to herself. 'Michael is almost human this morning.'

Michael was so engrossed in the riddle that he didn't see Mrs O'Shea's dog sunbathing on the pavement. He stumbled over it, and it made so much noise that Mrs O'Shea came running out to see who was hurting her dog.

'I wasn't hurting it,' protested Michael. 'I was reading this and I didn't see where I was putting my feet. Perhaps you can help me with it. It's a riddle.' he explained. Mrs O'Shea peered at the tattered envelope.

'Now, let me see. Lilies begins with L and Owls begins with O so Violets must begin with V, but I don't see what it means.'

'Nor do I, Mrs O'Shea, but thank you for your help, and I'm sorry I stood on your dog.' And off went Michael still puzzling over his tattered envelope.

Presently he sat down on the school wall just as the children came out to play.

'Hello Michael,' a little girl said to him. 'Have you had a letter?'

Now usually Michael would have told the little girl to go away, but he was so anxious to solve his riddle that he actually showed her the envelope. She read the words slowly for she was only just learning to read.

'L . . . O . . . V. That's easy!' she said. 'That's the word I put on my mum's birthday card, only it has an E at the end, like this.' She wrote the letters out large and clear for him.

'Perhaps the E comes from Everything. See! LOVE.'

'What's LOVE?' asked Michael.

'Don't you know what LOVE is? Did you never write it on your mum's birthday card?'

Michael shook his head miserably.

'Your Happy Battery must be flat,' said the little girl. 'It must be all flat and rusty.'

'I think it is, but I'm going to start putting it right. How do you think I should begin?'

'I think you've already started. You've just learned a new word, Michael!'

As Michael walked back up the village street Mrs O'Shea, Mrs O'Riley and the postman called out to him, 'Did you solve the riddle, Michael?'

Michael smiled for the first time for years.

'It's LOVE,' he said grinning from ear to ear.

'So it is!' they all said, and somewhere inside Michael McManus his Happy Battery began to hum. Suddenly sitting on his shoulder, was the little leprechaun.

'How many people did you talk to today, Michael?'

'Four . . . and a dog! It's been a very Happy Day. I'll have to try it again tomorrow, won't I?' but there was no reply. The little leprechaun had gone.

Simon and Ian

Simon and Ian had always been friends. You can't imagine two more different boys and it really was surprising that they enjoyed each others' company as much as they did. Simon was tall, strong and very good at sport. But he was not very good at school work. Ian was small and skinny and couldn't play any games well but he was brilliant at school work.

After school Simon and Ian would do things they both enjoyed. They might go pond dipping or take apples or carrots to the donkeys at the end of their lane. They could always find something to do together.

Trouble started the Monday before the half-term holiday.

'Starting on Wednesday,' said Mr Metcalf, their teacher, 'we will have a competition to see who is the champion at the times tables. There will be a rosette for the winner to be awarded on Friday. All 28 in the class will compete on Wednesday. The best fourteen will go to the semi-finals on Thursday. And the best seven of those will go to the final on Friday. Any questions?'

There were no questions but there were plenty of groans and Simon was one of the groaners. He hated competitions like this. Why couldn't they have a goal-kicking competition?

Ian, of course, was delighted.

Simon spent a good deal of time on Monday evening trying to memorize the times tables. He wrote them down and

read them. He said them out loud. He reminded himself that five always end in five or zero. He practised the finger play that reminded him of the nines.

Tuesday after school he and Ian studied together.

'Tomorrow it's the easy ones — two's and five's,' said Ian. Simon wasn't so sure they were easy.

Later that evening Simon was doodling with a biro. He made moustaches on the photos in the newspaper. He drew bird footprints across the palm of his hand. Then the prints disappeared up his shirt sleeve as if a tiny bird had gone to roost somewhere up there. And suddenly he had a terrible idea. What if he put the answers to the times tables on his wrists! Just in case - he probably wouldn't even look at them. They'd just be there to make him feel safe. . .

On Wednesday morning all the children in Mr Metcalf's room sat at their desks, waiting their turn to answer. A beautiful red rosette was pinned up for all to see. The winner would take it home on Friday.

Ian had every reason to hope it might be him. He was just about the best in the whole school at maths. It was something he could do!

Simon folded his hands loosely in his lap. He slowly and gently eased his wrists out of his sleeves and glanced down casually. The answers to two's to five's were there in neat rows. He felt safe. He wouldn't make a fool of himself anyway.

Mr Metcalf called on each of the children in turn. Some people answered straight away, others had to think.

149

'Simon. Two times seven?'

Easy. Simon didn't have to look. 'Fourteen.'

Next time round it was four times five. Not so easy but he knew it. 'Twenty.' The last time round it was five times nine. Difficult. He had to look. 'Forty-five.'

At the end of the first round both Simon and Ian were among the fourteen people who would go on to round two the next day. They were the only two who made no errors at all!

'I am pleasantly surprised, Simon,' said Mr Metcalf. 'I hope you will do as well tomorrow.'

It suddenly hit Simon that he would have to do even harder multiplications tomorrow.

'Shall I come round and help you study again tonight?' asked Ian.

'Ahhh, no thanks, Ian. I think I'll work harder on my own,' said Simon.

Simon spent a long time writing the answers to six's to nine's on his wrists.

The next day's competition was the same but the questions were harder. Simon had to look at his wrists several times. Once again he made no mistakes. He was the only one who didn't. Even Ian made one mistake.

'Simon! You're doing so well!' said Mr Metcalf.

'Well done, Simon,' said Ian but he sounded a bit sad.

On the way home Ian said, 'It looks like you might win this competition, Simon. You're lucky you can do so many things well. I was hoping to win that rosette. I've never won a rosette at sports day and I thought I might be able to win this one.'

Simon had never thought about that. It had never occured to him that if he cheated to win, someone who really deserved to win wouldn't. And worse than that, it was his best friend who would lose. On the other hand, if Simon won, Mr Metcalf and the other children would think he was good at school work after all. Ian was always the best in class. Maybe he wouldn't mind just this once if he wasn't the best. But the truth was, Ian was the best! Simon could win but he would never be the best. So winning would be a lie.

Simon spent a lot of time that evening thinking thoughts like this. He kept changing his mind about whether or not he would write the answers on his wrist. He even wrote them once and then washed them off again. He did notice that the ten's all ended in zero so he learned them off by heart. So maybe he could just cheat a little and write the eleven's and twelve's. Then he looked at the eleven's and saw how easy they were so he learned them off by heart, too. But the twelve's were difficult. He wrote them on his wrist. Such a little cheat couldn't hurt.

The next morning at school Simon felt good. He was going to win that rosette.

Then Simon saw Ian and began thinking again. He desperately wanted to win. He wanted to be good at times tables. But even if he did win he'd know he wasn't really good at times tables. He'd know Ian really deserved to win.

'Sir?' said Simon. 'Can I wash my hands before we begin? I got muddy coming to school.'

'Yes. Be quick, Simon.'

Simon rolled up his sleeves and scrubbed out the twelve's.

The final of the competition went very smoothly. Simon got his ten's and eleven's correct. He was really pleased with himself. But the twelve's? Well, he didn't get many of those correct. In fact, everyone except Ian missed some of the twelve's. He got them all correct. And all his ten's and eleven's as well. He won the rosette easily.

After school Simon couldn't stop telling Ian how well he had done.

'You didn't do so badly yourself,' said Ian. 'But I must say, I'm very pleased that I won!'

The best part was, they both felt good.

My Gran's Hat

My Gran's hat is older than I am. My Mum thinks it might even be older than she is. My Gran doesn't care how old it is. It's her hat and she likes it. It is shiny, navy-blue straw with a rolled back brim. She wears it right on top of her head with her lovely, curly, grey hair sprigging out all round it. Every once in a while she takes the old flowers off and puts new ones on. It's always blue flowers to match the hat. Mum says once she tried a feather but didn't like it. My Gran thinks she looks just fine in her hat. She doesn't. Not really. But no one would think of telling her. My grandad did once, a long time ago, and it made Gran furious. He's dead now and when she tells the story, she makes a joke about it. Gran's hat makes quite a few people laugh but they don't do it out loud because they don't want to hurt her feelings. Really, the only good thing about my Gran's hat is I can always find her in a crowd when she is wearing it. No one else has one like it.

For years and years, until she got too old to work hard, my Gran worked in the big house in our village. The people there really liked her and when their son was getting married, they invited Gran to the

wedding.

'You'll need a new dress,' said my Mum. She would have liked to say 'and a new hat' but she didn't.

'Do you think so?' asked Gran. 'It would be an expense.'

'There will be lots of people there, perhaps even some famous people. Have a new dress.'

Gran suggested they go to the shop in the village and see if they had something there to go with her hat. Mum and I cringed.

'This is a very special occasion.' said Mum. 'Let's really go shopping.'

The next Saturday we took the train to shop in the city. Gran wore her hat. We went in big department stores and little speciality shops. We were looking for Gran-sized, navy-blue things that went with that hat and suitable for wearing to weddings and we couldn't find a thing.

Mum would try to sound enthusiastic. 'What about this?'

Gran would finger it listlessly. 'No love. It's not me.'

Gran would say to the person serving that she wanted something to go with the hat. One look at Gran's hat and, 'Sorry, Madam, I don't think we can help you.'

The morning seemed endless. We were longing for lunch and finally Mum agreed we needed a break. We stopped looking for dresses and started looking for lunch. Gran likes nothing better than fish and chips out of a newspaper so Mum asked a traffic warden where there was a good chippie.

'The best one in the town is in Beggar's Passage. Turn into the little alleyway just past that shop - along there - Madame La Farge Boutique.' She pointed along the High Street.

It had begun to drizzle. The pavement was grey. The buildings were grey. The sky was grey. What a grey time we were having.

Suddenly, Gran caught her breath and stopped. Mum and I looked round and saw what she had seen. There in the window of Madam La Farge's Boutique was the most beautiful salmon-pink dress. And floating above it, held aloft like a flying saucer by a single, huge plume was the matching hat.

Gran only looked at the dress. Her grey eyes twinkled beneath her grey hair and shiny, navy-blue straw hat with rolled brim and last year's blue flowers and she said, 'But will it go with my hat?'

We're taught to always tell the truth, aren't we? Sometimes it might not seem the thing to do. I didn't think I'd ever be able to tell Gran the truth about her hat but the time had come to do just that.

'Gran,' I said taking her arm, 'it's about your hat. It's just not suitable. I know you like it but you really do need a new one.'

She didn't say anything. The three of us stood there, reflected in the shop window with that gorgeous hat hovering above that gorgeous dress.

Finally Gran said thoughtfully, 'You might be right . . . '

Mum saw her chance. 'Why not try them on together? Come on. Let's go in.'

We did. Madame La Farge had the dress in Gran's size. She buzzed around Gran, saying, 'Madame looks very lovely in salmon,' and 'Madame suits this length of skirt,' et cetera!

The dress was really lovely and we could see from Gran's face that she really wanted to go to the wedding in that dress.

Then the big question: 'Would Madame like to try the matching hat?'

Mum didn't let Gran answer. 'Yes, please!' she said.

'Come on , Gran,' I said. 'Off with the old and on with new!'

Gran carefully withdrew the long, old-fashioned hat pin that held her hat on and lifted off her hat and handed it to me to hold.

Madame La Farge glided into the fitting room holding the salmon-pink, wide-brimmed hat aloft. The plume tossed as if it were alive. Madam La Farge lowered it onto Gran's head. The plume settled. Gran looked hard. Neither Mum nor I could breathe. Gran looked absolutely beautiful. She still looked like Gran but special.

Gran turned to look at me, tossing the plume around, and said, 'You're right. I do need a new hat!'

So that was that. Fish and chips. Train home. Many oohs and ahhs from the family about the dress and especially the hat. But it's not quite the end of the story.

Gran went to the wedding in her salmon-pink dress and hat. She managed to borrow a matching bag from Auntie Dorie. It was quite a big bag. As I was walking her to the church on the big day I asked her why she needed such a big bag. She opened it and inside there was the shiny, navy straw with rolled brim and last year's blue flowers.

'Just in case,' she said.

No Charge

One Saturday morning after breakfast Michael's mother asked him to dry the dishes because she had a busy day ahead. Reluctantly, Michael agreed. With a lot of clattering the job was eventually finished. Michael went upstairs to play but then he had an idea. He found a pencil and a piece of paper and wrote something down.

After dinner he surprised his parents by offering to dry the dishes again. Once again, as soon as he had finished, he went upstairs and added another line of writing to the paper. Exactly the same thing happened after tea.

Later that evening Michael changed into his pyjamas and dressing-gown and went downstairs for his supper. After slowly sipping his milky drink he kissed his mother and father goodnight. As he was leaving he took the piece of paper out of his dressing-gown pocket and placed it on the table in front of his mother. He then skipped from the room and went to bed.

His mother, full of curiosity, picked up the paper and started to read it. As she did the expression on her faced changed. She looked sad as she silently passed the note to her husband. At first he thought it was quite amusing but then realised that his wife was upset. He read the paper again. It said:

Mother owes Michael:

For drying breakfast dishes 20p

154

For drying dinner dishes 20p
For drying tea dishes 20p

Total   60p

'The ungrateful boy!' he exclaimed. 'I've a good mind to go up there and give him a good talking to. It's not asking much to dry a few dishes. When I think what you do for him!'

Michael's mother said 'No, dear. I've got a better idea.'

She took a piece of paper and wrote for about five minutes. When she had finished she folded the paper carefully, quietly climbed the stairs and placed it on the bed-side cupboard of the now sleeping Michael..

Next morning, Michael woke up before his parents. He was surprised to find the piece of paper on his cupboard. He opened it and read:

Michael owes Mother:

For cooking three meals a day: Nothing
For dusting and cleaning your bed-room: Nothing
For washing and ironing your clothes:
                               Nothing
For acting as nurse when you are ill:
                               Nothing
For many other jobs: Nothing

Total: Nothing

Michael rushed downstairs, grabbed his bill which was still lying on the table and tore it up. He rushed back upstairs still holding the pieces. He woke his mother with a gentle shake and slowly let the pieces fall into the waste-paper basket.

'I'm sorry, Mum.' With these words he jumped on the bed and gave his mother a huge hug.

The Bully

'Ha-Ha! Duckfoot! Hey, you, new kid! Why do you walk like a duck?! Ha-Ha!'

Stephen could hear the boys behind him laughing. He already knew the name of the biggest boy. It was Richard. It was only Stephen's first day at his new school and already he knew who to be careful of.

Stephen opened the front door of his new home.

'Hello, Stephen,' said his Mum. 'How was it today?'

'Alright,' said Stephen but he was missing his old friends at his old school very much. 'There are some pretty unfriendly boys in my class. I hope I'll be able to make new friends.'

'I'm sure you will,' said his Mum. 'Give it time.'

The next day Stephen was in the boys' cloakroom when Richard came in. He was on his own so Stephen ventured, 'Hello, Richard.'

'Who do you think you're talking to, Duckfoot?' said Richard and he pushed Stephen against the basins.

Stephen didn't want to cry but his ribs hurt, and he hurt on the inside, too, because he wanted to belong and have friends.

'Are you alright, Stephen?' asked his teacher.

Just then Richard came back into the room. He was looking right at him so Stephen just nodded. He knew if he said anything about what happened he would really be in trouble with Richard after school.

At playtime, Richard organized a football match. No one could play unless he said so. All the children who wanted to play were being nice to Richard. Stephen edged his way into the group of children who were asking Richard what team they should be on and what position they should play. Richard held the ball under his arm.

When he saw Stephen he said, 'Get out of here, Duckfoot! You're not playing!'

Some of the other children supported Richard by saying, 'Yeh, go on. We've got enough players.'

Stephen felt terrible. He realized that Richard was the boss. Everyone was afraid of him so they did what he said. Richard knew it and he liked it that way. Stephen thought he would have to try to make friends somehow. He just couldn't stand being lonely and left out.

For a few days Stephen hung back, just hovering on the edge of the group that was always around Richard. Then one day when the group was wandering around the playground with nothing much to do, Richard ran up to a little child who was bouncing a ball and counting the bounces. He took the child's ball and ran off with it, laughing and teasing. He lost control of the ball and it bounced away and rolled right to Stephen. Stephen picked up the ball.

The little child who had been playing with it came up to Stephen. 'Can I have my ball, please?' she said.

Stephen was about to give it to her when

Richard shouted, 'Give it here, Duckfoot!'

Stephen thought quickly. Here was his chance to get in good with Richard.

He threw the ball to Richard.

'OK, Duckfoot!' shouted Richard. Stephen felt part of the group at last.

As the days went by Richard teased Stephen less and so the other boys stopped teasing him as well. He became part of the group, or 'the gang' as they called themselves. But always there was a threat hanging over Stephen. If he didn't do what Richard wanted him to he knew he would be pushed out of the group and bullied again.

One day when Stephen was passing the teachers' cloakroom, he looked in and saw Richard with his hand in one of the teachers' coat pockets. He couldn't believe his eyes.

Richard looked right at him and whispered, 'One word, Duckfoot, and I'll poke your eyes out!'

Stephen fled, shaking, back to the classroom. He knew Richard was stealing. He knew he should tell someone but he was afraid. For the rest of the day Stephen could think of nothing else.

Just before the end of school the headteacher came round to all the classes. He said, 'I seem to have dropped five pounds out of my pocket somewhere in school today. If anyone finds it I'd be very pleased to have it back.'

Stephen looked at Richard. Richard was smiling a small, sneaky smile. When he saw Stephen looking at him he shook a fist at him.

Stephen was frightened. He wanted friends but he didn't want to help Richard

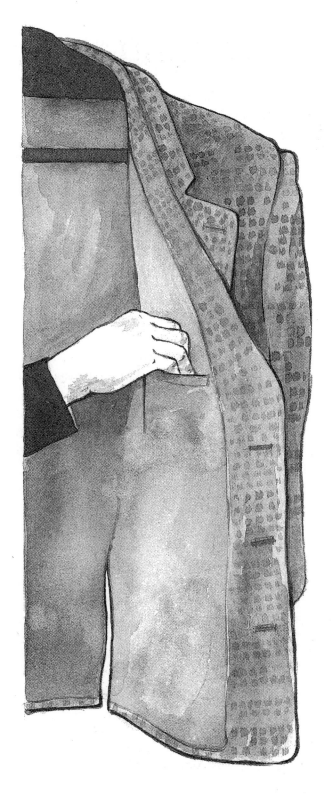

steal. He was afraid of what Richard might do to him if he told. He knew what he had to do and he hoped the headteacher would help him with his problem with Richard. He knew Richard was watching him so he went to the teacher and asked in a loud voice if he could got to the toilet. Instead of going to the toilet he went straight to the headteacher and told him what he had seen and why he hadn't said anything at the time. That was all he had to do.

'Thank you, Stephen,' said the headteacher. 'Please don't worry. I will talk with Richard and sort things out. No one will know you have told me what you saw.'

The headteacher took Richard into his office and closed the door.

After that, Richard was away from school for two days. While he was gone everyone had a nice time working and playing together in a friendly way. The headteacher kept his promise and when Richard did come back to school he tried to be friendly, too.

Nasim's Eid Gift

Nasim had had a fine time celebrating Eid with his family. They had marked the Muslim day of thanksgiving by going to the mosque together and giving money to the poor. An important part of the celebration of Eid was sharing with people less fortunate than yourself. There had been lots of special foods and Nasim had especially enjoyed the variety of sweets they always had at Eid. And they had also exchanged gifts. Nasim's best gift was a wonderful set of colouring pens he had wanted for a long time.

But, like all holidays, Eid came to an end and Nasim was back at school.

'Hello, Nasim,' said his teacher, welcoming him back. 'Did you have an enjoyable Eid?'

'Yes, thank you. I did.'

'Good,' said his teacher. 'I see you've brought something with you from the celebration.'

Nasim had brought a large plate of the special Eid foods to share with the other children. While his teacher passed the plate round, Nasim showed the children some of the gifts he had received. They particularly admired the giant set of colouring pens which contained almost every shade imaginable. Nasim was looking forward to using them and sharing them with his friends. The plate came back empty and everyone was smacking their lips at the good tastes of the Eid food. Nasim took his gifts and the plate and put them into his school bag and hung it on his peg in the hall.

Back home that afternoon, he unpacked his bag on the kitchen table so that he could get his homework done before his favourite TV programmes began. He looked into his bag, blinked and looked again.

'It's gone! My colouring set has disappeared! Mum, someone must have taken it!' He burst into tears and hugged his mother, who comforted him until he stopped crying.

'Never mind,' she said kindly. 'We could always get you another set. Perhaps you left them at school by accident.'

Next morning Nasim asked his teacher to help him find them. When she asked the class if they knew what had happened to them, there was silence to begin with. Then a voice from the back of the room piped up.

'I took them, miss, but I only borrowed them.' It was Christopher, a boy whose father was in prison for burglary. Although he did not have any real friends, he appeared to be happy to be left on his own. He stood, walked over to Nasim and gave him back his pen set. 'Here you are, Nasim. I meant to ask you, but you were busy playing with your friends . . . Sorry.' He paused, lowered his head and returned to his seat.

The teacher frowned at him but said nothing more.

At playtime, some of the boys began to tease Christopher.

'You nicked those pens. You must be

a thief.'

'Just like your dad; he's a thief, isn't he?'

Christopher ran off to a corner of the playground and kicked a stone around, whilst the other children ignored him. When he went back into school, Nasim noticed that his face was tear-stained.

At home time, Nasim waited at the gate for Christopher to come out. When Christopher saw him, he said, 'I suppose you want a fight, do you?'

'No Christopher, I wanted to give you these.' He handed the boy his new set of pens. Christopher looked at them and then looked at Nasim in amazement.

'But . . . But, they're your new pens!'

'I know, and I want you to have them.'

'But why? I thought you would be really angry with me for taking them. Everyone thinks I stole them, but I didn't. I really did mean to give them back.'

'I know and I believe you. I can always get another set so I thought you would like them.'

Christopher took the pens and for the first time since his father had gone to prison, he smiled. He felt a warm glow grow inside him as he realised that he was Nasim's new friend.

My Teacher Hates Me

The road to school was long and full of interesting things. Leonard meandered along. He stood and watched the postman dance around as Mr Melrose's corgi snapped around his ankles. He stood and watched the window cleaner strap his long ladder to his short bike and then wobble off up the road. He stood and watched as the sun slowly appeared from behind one cloud and then disappeared behind another.

When Leonard finally sauntered through the school gates, the playground was empty. Of course it was. The bell had rung ten minutes before. Leonard shrugged and made his way to the classroom.

Mr Henson's eyes narrowed as Leonard walked through the door. His moustache bristled, his thin, bony face twitched.

'Late again, Leonard?' He didn't wait for Leonard to answer. 'It's no good, Leonard. You come in late every day. You will never understand the lesson if you are not here for the start of it. Now sit down and get on with some maths.'

Mr Henson hates me, thought Leonard. Maths. Mr Henson only loves maths!

'Leonard!' shouted Mr Henson, interrupting Leonard's dark thoughts. 'Will you *please* pay attention!'

Leonard found maths very difficult. His brain tripped over numbers. The other children seemed to enjoy maths the way

Mr Henson taught it but to Leonard it was all a huge mystery.

When dinnertime bell went, Leonard was the first out into the freedom of the playground. He liked football so much more than maths. Leonard wasn't great at it but at least he knew what he was supposed to do.

Leonard got the ball and he was well placed for the shot.

'Go on, Len, shoot!' the others urged. Leonard kicked the ball hard. It flew in a high arc and plummeted down towards earth. Sadly, between the falling ball and the earth, Mr Henson's head had appeared. The ball smacked him straight on the top of his head and he staggered backwards, not so much from the force of the ball as from its unexpectedness. At first Mr Henson frowned and a furious roar seemed inevitable. But instead of roaring he simply rubbed his head and smiled. It was a small watery smile but a smile all the same. And all the boys were grateful for it. All the boys, that is, except Leonard who was nowhere to be seen.

Even before the ball had bounced off Mr Henson's head, Leonard had turned and run through the playground gates and across the road.

Everybody in the playground heard the screech of brakes as the tanker swerved to avoid Leonard. Everybody heard the crash, the crunch of metal, the splintering of wood - and then there was a sickening silence. They rushed to see what had happened and arrived at the gate to see the dust settling on the overturned petrol tanker as it lay partly beneath the now demolished advertising hoardings that

had faced the school. As they watched they saw the driver of the tanker climb from his cabin dazed and shaken but unhurt. Then they suddenly became aware of the ooze of petrol spreading from the wreckage.

Mr Henson pushed past the boys and raced across to the driver.

'The boy . . . !' the driver shouted in Mr Henson's face. 'The boy . . . !' and he pointed at the tangle of collapsed hoarding. 'Under there!' And then, sniffing the air, his eyes widened with fear. Leaving Mr Henson, the driver rushed across the road, gesturing to the boys to go back into the playground. 'Get back!' he shouted. 'Get back before it blows! Call 999!'

The boys needed no further warning, they rushed back and pushed their way into the school building. The headmaster who was almost trampled by this stampede, pieced together the story from their hurried accounts and immediately phoned for the emergency services.

Meanwhile Leonard lay in a confusion of dust and darkness. His leg hurt and he couldn't move it. The noise of the crash had been enormous and frightening, but this dark silence was worse. His nostrils were almost scorched by the smell of petrol. He began to whimper with the fear and pain, but as much as he would have liked to shout out and scream he couldn't.

And then there was a voice. It was a calm, comforting voice.

'Are you in there, Len? It's me, Mr Henson.'

'Yes, Mr Henson.'

'Don't try to move. Someone'll get you out soon. Are you hurt?'

'It's my leg: my leg hurts and it's trapped.'

'Just lie still until they move this wood, you'll be alright then.'

'What's the smell of petrol?'

'Don't worry about that, Len, it's nothing. Just don't light a cigarette, that's all!'

Leonard grinned.

Mr Henson spoke again. 'Tell me your five times table, Len.'

Leonard couldn't believe his ears, but Mr Henson repeated, 'Come on, your fives, surely you can do that!'

'One five is five, two fives are ten, three fives . . . '

Leonard chanted the table, his voice growing louder and more confident as he did so. When he'd finished Mr Henson prompted him again.

'Sixes.'

'I don't know the sixes.'

'Try!'

'One six is six, two sixes are . . . ' and he struggled slowly through to the end, urged on by Mr Henson.

He was halfway through the nine times table before the rescuers came and by then he wasn't sure what he was being rescued from - the pile of broken wood or Mr Henson's maths.

And then the wood was lifted and he found himself blinking in the sudden sunlight. He was lifted onto a stretcher and carried to the ambulance which was parked some way from the wreckage.

'You were lucky the whole thing didn't blow up,' said the ambulanceman. 'You and your teacher would be goners by now.'

Leonard had plenty of time to think about these words as he lay in the back of the ambulance. Later as he lay in the hospital bed with his leg in plaster, he laughed and said to his mother. 'Mr Henson made me do maths while I was trapped. Maths! He really *must* hate me!'

The House with Golden Windows

David had been very excited when, at the age of eight, he was told that the family was moving to a new home. His parents had decided to move away from the town and settle in the countryside.

The family arrived at their new home in the morning. David was most impressed. It was a tall white house set in a large garden. They opened all the doors and windows to let in some fresh air and then waited for the removal van to arrive with their furniture. David was eager to see his new bedroom and rushed upstairs. he was delighted because not only was it much larger than he had imagined but also from his window he had the most wonderful view. The house was built on a hillside overlooking a valley with a river meandering its way slowly to the sea. On the other side of the valley was a range of hills, dotted with houses and patches of woodland. As he looked across the valley David's gaze was attracted by a beautiful white house which seemed to have windows of polished gold.

David quickly settled down to his new life. He soon made friends with the village children and he spent many happy hours with them exploring the countryside close to his home. He sowed vegetable seeds in garden and waited excitedly for them to grow. It was a rewarding moment when he picked his first peas and brought them for his mother to cook. It was an ideal place for a child to grow up in and David was very happy there.

But he couldn't help wondering about the house with the golden windows. Every morning when he drew back the curtains, he looked across the valley at that house. If the sun was shining, the white walls sparkled and the windows glowed. He wondered who could live in such an exciting and magical place. He wondered what

kind of garden it had. He imagined it must be an even nicer place to live than his own home. David promised himself that one day he would visit the house and find out what sort of wonderful place it was.

Five years later, when he was thirteen, his opportunity came. During the summer holidays his mother let him go on a cycle ride with one of his friends. David knew exactly where he wanted to go. Many times in the past five years he had pinpointed his 'dream house' on his father's Ordnance Survey map and memorised the route he would follow to reach it. His Mum gave them a picnic lunch and by eleven o'clock they were ready for their adventure. Before leaving, David ran upstairs to his bedroom and took a long look at the house on the other side of the valley which looked as beautiful as ever, bathed in the morning sunlight.

They freewheeled down the hill until they reached the main road which followed the river the four miles to the nearby town. The bridge there was the only crossing point over the river in the area. David led the way and his friend was amazed that he knew the route so well.

With mounting excitement David realized they were very close to the house with the golden windows. Another turn in the road and he would be in front of the house he had been curious about ever since that first day he had seen it from the window of his new bedroom. Finally they were there. The two boys propped their cycles against a tree. David raced to the gateway of the house. He looked along the drive towards the big white house. At first he thought he must be in the wrong place.

It *was* a fine house but not the magical, exciting place he had seen from across the valley. The white walls did not glisten and the windows were made of ordinary glass.

'It's no different than out house,' he said to himself. This thought prompted him to look across the valley. His attention was caught by a beautiful white house with windows made golden by the afternoon sun. He realized he was seeing his own house. It looked just as magical and exciting as this house had always looked. David realized just how lucky he was to live in such a wonderful place.

O Christmas Tree

The little fir tree had always been small. It was surrounded by bigger trees and didn't get enough sunlight or moisture to allow it to grow properly. At least the other trees had protected it from the cold winds of winter. They did, that is, until one day they were all chopped down. The little fir tree heard the woodcutters saying they were going to be used as masts for sailing ships.

Now the little fir tree was all alone. It had to face the cold winter winds by itself. The days grew shorter. The nights were long and cold. One day the sky went dark grey, snow fell fast and the little tree's world was blanketed.

Soon afterwards, excited voices came across the forest clearing. Two children appeared, walking with their father, the head woodcutter. They were laughing and dancing about in the fresh snow. Their father walked right toward the little fir tree. 'There it is!' he exclaimed, pointing with his spade. 'I told you it was just the right size for our cottage.' Carefully, he dug up the little fir tree, making sure none of its roots were damaged. With the noisy children running ahead, the woodcutter carried the little fir tree back to their cottage where it was planted in a large bucket. For the next three weeks the little fir tree had a wonderful time. It thoroughly enjoyed being the centre of attention with all its glittering decorations and fairy lights. Occasionally it thought of its grand friends probably somewhere at sea but it was no longer envious. It was sure they would happily change places with it if they had been small enough. Each afternoon as darkness fell the little tree looked forward to its lights being switched on and to hearing the family exclaim how beautiful it was.

Twelve days after Christmas the little tree had a shock. The children took the decorations off it and packed away the fairy lights. The tree became terribly worried when it was carried outside, still in its bucket, and left in the garden. The little tree would have been even more anxious if it had known what was happening to most other Christmas trees at the same time.

When the woodcutter came home that evening he replanted the little fir tree in the cottage garden and the children promised to decorate it every year with outside fairy lights.

This happened a long time ago, so by now the tree must be very tall and grand and, if the promise has been kept, it must be a beautiful sight for everyone who passes the cottage at Christmas time.

Micro Mikey

James stumped up the steps to his front door. He slid the key into the lock and let himself in. He knew no one was home. No one ever was when he came in from school. He dropped his school bag by the front door; dropped his coat on top of it. He walked to the kitchen as if he had been programmed. Freezer door - open. Microwave chips - out. Microwave door - open. Microwave chips - in. Buzz. Hummm. Ding! Microwave chips - out. Salt. Vinegar. Mouth - open. Slurp. Crunch. Always the same.

Still crunching. James dragged himself to his computer. He switched on and plugged in Micro Mikey. Always the same. James had played Micro Mikey so many times it was no longer a challenge. It was if James himself was programmed like Micro Mikey. The colourful maze with its poison pits and precipices, its monsters and mammoth mosquitoes flashed onto the screen. Green slime wiggled over quicksand and magenta lightning split the black sky. It was not nearly as exciting as it used to be for James. He played out of habit.

Micro Mikey appeared, flexing his tiny muscles. he ran in jerks, the right foot poking out in front and the left foot to the back. Always the same. He plummeted into the pits and fought off mosquitoes. He leapt over slime and punched away the lightning. The computer beeped and squeaked and buzzed and hummed. James yawned and fiddled with the controls.

'Hey! James!' came a voice from the machinery in front of James.

'Huh? Who said that?' said James peering behind his computer.

'Me! I said that!' Micro Mikey was standing in the middle of the screen with his hands on his hips. 'This is so boring! Don't you think this is boring? We do this day after day. I am totally fed up with crashing about in slime and somersaulting over precipices. Why don't you give me a rest?! Do something else once in a while!'

James was speechless. He didn't know what to do.

'Hey, James. Let me out - just for a little while. Come on, James! Let me out.'

'What . . .? How . . .? Let you out? You mean you're real?'

'Of course I'm real - sort of real. Let me out.'

'How?'

Micro Mikey told James the very secret access code. James pressed the proper keys and the computer made a sharp pop — a noise James had never heard it make before — and there on the keyboard stood Micro Mikey. He was still his same size and when he smiled up at James a toothy grin flashed onto his tiny face.

'Thank you, James!'

James was speechless. He timidly reached out a finger and tried to feel Micro Mikey. He felt of nothing except a tiny electric prickle.

'I'm here but I'm not here,' teased Micro Mikey. And with that he disappeared.

'Hey!' gasped James. 'Come back!'

Micro Mikey reappeared. 'I didn't go anywhere. I just turned sideways. I'm only two dimensional so when I turn sideways -' he did it again to demonstrate, '- I disappear,' he said reappearing.

Delight suddenly gripped James. He laughed. He couldn't think of what to say. 'Have a micro chip,' he said pushing a cold chip at Micro Mikey.

'That's not what I call a micro chip,' said Mikey. 'Micro chips are what make this thing go and you certainly can't eat them.'

'What do you eat?' asked James, curious about his new friend.

'Light, electricity - dead boring stuff really.'

'What do you do when I'm not making you fight all the creatures and the gunge?' asked James.

'Wait for you to turn on this flipping machine. What do you do when your not making me do all that stuff?'

'I don't know - nothing much. I just get through the day till I can come home and turn you on.'

They thought for a moment.

'Do you think,' offered Mikey, 'as long as I'm out, we might do something else for a change?'

It was the most exciting invitation James had ever had. Micro Mikey never went back into his two dimensional computer environment. James never played the Micro Mikey game again. Mikey showed James more exciting things he could do with his computer and James showed Mikey the real world.

I wonder what kind of things in your real world you would show Micro Mikey if he came out of a computer to play with you.

168

Poppy Day

'Look,' said William to his teacher as he crossed the playground before the morning bell. 'I've got a poppy, too. I put 20p in my Grandad's collection tin and he gave it to me. Where did you get yours?'

'A woman was selling poppies outside the library. I got mine from her,' answered Mrs Eddy.

Amy came over. 'I've got one, too.'

'My Mum gave me hers,' said John. 'Why does everyone have them?'

'The money from selling poppies goes to help war veterans,' said Mrs Eddy.

'What's a veteran?' asked Amy.

'It's someone who fought in a war. We honour the veterans in November.'

'Why November?'

'Because the Great War ended on the eleventh of November. It was called Armistice Day and that was the day the countries fighting agreed to stop the war. Now we honour the veterans of all wars on the anniversary of that armistice. To show we care about them, we buy and wear poppies.'

'Why poppies?'

'During the Great War . . . ,' began Mrs Eddy.

'My great-grandad fought in that war,' interrupted William. 'He's almost a hundred years old!'

Before Mrs Eddy could finish what she was going to say, the morning bell rang. Just before lunch Mrs Eddy said, 'This morning in the playground, we were talking about Poppy Day. There is something in the wood nearby that might help you understand about Poppy Day and the Great War. I am going to walk there after I eat my lunch. If anyone would like to come, meet me by the front door — and wear your wellies.'

Afterwards Mrs Eddy and eleven eager walkers set out along a muddy bridle path into the wood at the top of the hill. The wood that was part of a scout camp.

'I've been here camping,' said John.

'Generations of boys have had fun in these woods,' said Mrs Eddy.

The bridle path was squelchy with mud and their wellies slithered and sucked with every step. They turned off the main path along a narrow track.

Finally Mrs Eddy stopped under a huge oak. Nearby, amidst the tangle of the wood was a monument of some sort. It was made of brick and blocks of stone.

It was surrounded by a low, rusty iron fence. The small gate hung off its hinges. The group filed through and up the wide steps. There were some words cut into the stone. They were mossy and chipped in places. William and Amy began to work out what it said.

' "In . . Loving . . Mem . ." What's this?'

'Can you read it for us, Mrs Eddy? It's hard to make it out.'

Mrs Eddy stood in front of the monument. ' "In loving memory of a youthful band who . . ." '

'What's a youthful band?'

'It's a young group,' said Mrs Eddy. 'In this case it means boy scouts.' She continued to read. . . ' "who played as children amid these woods and heaths. In the Great War for their country and for mankind they fell before their time. But wherever they now lie here they are never far." '

'What does it mean, Mrs Eddy?'

'It means there were scouts who came here when they were children. They had lots of fun in these woods just like scouts today have. When the First World War happened, they went to fight. A lot of them were killed. Millions of men were killed in that war. It went on for years and neither side made any progress toward winning. Still, the leaders on both sides kept sending men into battle. They fought in the worst possible conditions. They lived in trenches dug into muddy ground . . .'

'Like the bridle path we just came along?' ventured Amy.

'Much worse than that,' said Mrs Eddy. 'And they had to dig trenches in mud like

that and live in them. And the trenches filled up with water and more mud. They fought against terrible weapons - machine guns, mortar fire, clouds of poison gas. Most of them must have been very afraid. I don't think any of us can imagine how awful it was.'

Everyone was quiet. Then John said, 'Do you mean that boys like us had to go to war?'

'Not boys as young as you. Eighteen might seem old to you but when you are eighteen you will realize it is far too young to die. But boys that young were sent into the trenches to fight. "They fell before their time . . ." means they died before they should have done - they died very young. Some families lost all their men - fathers and sons died in the same battle. Brothers fought side by side and died together in the mud. After the war there were villages in which not a single man was left.'

'So my great grandad is lucky,' said William.

'Yes, he is! And you are lucky to have him,' said Mrs Eddy. 'And the ones who died were buried far from home, near the battlefields where they fell. But what about this bit? " . . . wherever they now lie, here they are never far." What do you think that means?'

The children thought for a minute. Then Amy said, 'I think it means that even if they are dead and buried far away, their spirits are in this place because we are thinking about them when we see this monument.'

Everyone nodded and murmured their agreement.

'But what about the poppies?' asked John.

'After the war was over, the armies went home. The land where they had fought was completely ruined. Nothing grew there. It looked like nothing could ever grow there again. But like soldiers' wounds that healed, the land began to heal, too. The trenches filled in. The mud dried up. Slowly, green things began to show themselves. Among the first plants to appear were field poppies. They came up and flowered - acres and acres of them. The fields bloomed with blood-red poppies as if to remind people of the suffering that had taken place there. And so we wear our poppies to show we remember.'

Everyone was quiet. Then William said, 'Will there be another war, Miss? Will I have to fight in a war?'

'I don't know, William. But I do know if people remember how terrible war is, it is less likely they will let it happen again.'

Dear Diary

Thursday: It's official: Mr Thomas is getting married. My team came first in the multiplication race in Maths. Richard and Jane asked me to go swimming tomorrow after school. I had to say no because I have to pack my things. I go to Dad and Caroline's tomorrow night.

Friday: Down with Mr Thomas. I hope he gets lost on his honeymoon. I couldn't decide what to take with me to Dad's. Caroline doesn't like messes so I didn't pack my paints or my chemistry set. I can't remember which plaid shirt Dad gave me for Christmas so I wasn't sure which one to take. Don't want to hurt his feelings. Mum and Stevie won't want me turning up to get things I forgot. Hope I remembered everything. And why do I have to call him 'Stevie' — yuk. 'Steve' is much better.

Saturday: The room here is so small and tidy. Dad is tidier than he ever was when we all lived together like a normal family. I miss my chips! You never get chips here. Lots of yogurt and lentils -—not half bad the way Caroline cooks them but I do love my chips!

Sunday: Went to a concert last night. Never had a moment alone. I think Dad and Caroline think I'm just a little kid. But the concert was good. Raining today. I wouldn't mind a nice splash round in the puddles but it's not on.

Monday — Bank Holiday: An extra day with Dad and Caroline. I beat them both at Monopoly! I had hotels everywhere. Dad asked me what I want for my birthday. Caroline made some suggestions but I think Dad was a bit cheesed off with her for butting in. She wouldn't like to hear what I really want — a day with my Mum and Dad together. I know it could never be like old times but I get fed up with bouncing back and forth. I love them both and I'd like to love them both at the same time for a change. I tried to tell Dad. I'm not sure what he thought about it. Packed up to go back to Mum and Stevie's.

Tuesday: Got here late last night and crawled in under my lovely old duvet still in my clothes. Mum and Stevie had some friends round so they didn't mind me going to bed right away. School was a drag. Mr Thomas must have had a row with his beloved as he seemed in a foul mood. Lovely sausage, egg and chips for supper. Stevie certainly can put the chips away. After supper he played the piano and sang for a bit.

Wednesday: Rain again. Mum at a demonstration today so I did my own tea and hers. She came home soaked and tired. Stevie at his upholstery class tonight. Mum asked me what I want for my birthday. I tried to explain to her like I did to Dad. She got cross. Said it could never be the same again. I said I knew that. I said she doesn't have to love Dad and he doesn't have to love her but I love them both and I want to have us together for my birthday. Went to my room and stayed there. Threw darts at he target on the back of my door. Hit the door more than the target. Don't care!

Thursday: Mr Thomas was sweet as can be today. Must have patched it up with Miss X. When I got home from school Mum was on the phone with Dad and they were having a row. Afterwards, Mum called it a discussion. I remember those discussions from before the divorce.

Friday: Well, my birthday is tomorrow. The cards have started coming in the post. Not only from my real grandparents but even from Caroline and from Stevie's parents. Not bad. They sang 'Happy Birthday' to me in school — Mr Thomas' idea. He's not so bad after all. No sign of any big bags or boxes coming into the house. I thought I would be going to Dad and Caroline's but Mum told me not to bother to pack.

Saturday: HAPPY BIRTHDAY TO ME! What an incredible day it has been! Mum and Stevie took me to the fun fair at the seaside. I can't believe it! Dad and Caroline were there to meet us! It was all planned! We all went on the rides. Mum and Dad both stayed with me all the time. Caroline and Stevie walked and talked together and let us three just be a family. It was the best birthday ever. AND NO ONE FOUGHT ABOUT ANYTHING!!!

Thematic Index